# TEACHER EDITION • Chapter 10

## Convert Units of Measure



Houghton Mifflin Harcourt

Printed in the U.S.A.

ISBN 978-0-544-29542-1

4 5 6 7 8 9 10 1678 22 21 20 19 18 17 16 15
4500529853 B C D E F G

# Critical Area Geometry and Measurement

CRITICAL AREA Developing understanding of volume



Domain: **Measurement and Data** 5.MD

| Lessons | Grade 5 Common Core State Standards |
|---|---|
| | Cluster A: **Convert like measurement units within a given measurement system.** |
| 10.1–10.7 | 5.MD.A.1 Convert among different-sized standard measurement units within a given measurement system (e.g., convert 5 cm to 0.05 m), and use these conversions in solving multi-step, real world problems. |

# Table of Contents

## Chapter 10 Convert Units of Measure

**Domain:**
Measurement and Data 5.MD

**MP1** Make sense of problems and persevere in solving them.
**MP2** Reason abstractly and quantitatively.
**MP3** Construct viable arguments and critique the reasoning of others.
**MP4** Model with mathematics.
**MP5** Use appropriate tools strategically.
**MP6** Attend to precision.
**MP7** Look for and make use of structure.
**MP8** Look for and express regularity in repeated reasoning.

# Chapter At A Glance

**Domain: Measurement and Dat**

**Chapter Essential Question** What strategies can you use to compare and convert measurements?

Use the *Go Math! Planning Guide* for correlations, math practices information, and more.

## Lesson At A Glance

| | 1 Day LESSON 10.1 — 5.MD.A.1 | 1 Day LESSON 10.2 — 5.MD.A.1 | 1 Day LESSON 10.3 — 5.MD.A.1 |
|---|---|---|---|
| |  |  |  |
| Essential Question | How can you compare and convert customary units of length? | How can you compare and convert customary units of capacity? | How can you compare and convert customary units of weight? |
| Objective | Compare, contrast, and convert customary units of length. | Compare, contrast, and convert customary units of capacity. | Compare, contrast, and convert customary units of weight. |
| Vocabulary | foot, inch, mile, yard | **capacity**, cup, fluid ounce, gallon, pint, quart | ounce, pound, ton, **weight** |
| ELL Strategy | ELL **Strategy** • Rephrase | ELL **Strategy** • Understand Context | ELL **Strategy** • Identify Relationships |

GO DIGITAL — Go online to access all your chapter resources

www.thinkcentral.com

| | | |
|---|---|---|
| 10.1 *i*Student Edition | 10.2 *i*Student Edition | 10.3 *i*Student Edition |
| 10.1 eTeacher Edition | 10.2 eTeacher Edition | 10.3 eTeacher Edition |
|  Personal Math Trainer |  Personal Math Trainer | 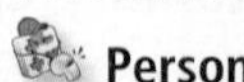 Personal Math Trainer |
|  Math on the Spot Video |  Math on the Spot Video |  Math on the Spot Video |
|  Animated Math Models |  Animated Math Models | Real World Video, Ch. 10 |
|  *i*Tools | *i*Tools |  Animated Math Models |
| 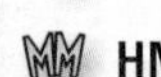 HMH Mega Math | 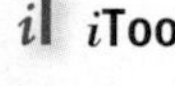 HMH Mega Math | *i*Tools |

Print Resources

| | | |
|---|---|---|
| 10.1 Student Edition | 10.2 Student Edition | 10.3 Student Edition |
| 10.1 Practice and Homework (in the *Student Edition*) | 10.2 Practice and Homework (in the *Student Edition*) | 10.3 Practice and Homework (in the *Student Edition*) |
| 10.1 Reteach (in the *Chapter Resources*) | 10.2 Reteach (in the *Chapter Resources*) | 10.3 Reteach (in the *Chapter Resource* |
| 10.1 Enrich (in the *Chapter Resources*) | 10.2 Enrich (in the *Chapter Resources*) | 10.3 Enrich (in the *Chapter Resources*) |
| Grab-and-Go™ Centers Kit | Grab-and-Go™ Centers Kit | Grab-and-Go™ Centers Kit |

RtI Response to Intervention

| Before the Chapter | During the Lesson | After the Chapter |
|---|---|---|
| **Show What You Know** | **Share and Show** | **Chapter Review/Test** |
| • Prerequisite Skills Activities<br>• Personal Math Trainer | • Reteach<br>• Mid-Chapter Checkpoint<br>• Personal Math Trainer<br>• Reteach Activity (online) | • Reteach<br>• Personal Math Trainer<br>• Reteach Activity (online) |

## Chapter Pacing Chart

| Introduction | Instruction | Assessment | Total |
|---|---|---|---|
| 1 day | 7–8 days | 2 days | 10–11 days |

**1 Day**

**LESSON 10.4**  5.MD.A.1

### Multistep Measurement Problems. . . . . . . . . .603A

How can you solve multistep problems that include measurement conversions?

Convert measurement units to solve multistep problems.

**ELL Strategy** • Understand Context

10.4 *i*Student Edition
10.4 *e*Teacher Edition
Personal Math Trainer
Math on the Spot Video
Animated Math Models
*i*Tools
HMH Mega Math

10.4 Student Edition
10.4 Practice and Homework (in the *Student Edition*)
10.4 Reteach (in the *Chapter Resources*)
10.4 Enrich (in the *Chapter Resources*)
Grab-and-Go™ Centers Kit

**1 Day**

**LESSON 10.5** 5.MD.A.1

### Metric Measures. . . . .611A

How can you compare and convert metric units?

Compare, contrast, and convert metric units.

**dekameter**, centimeter, decimeter, gram, kilogram, kilometer, liter, mass, meter, milligram, milliliter, millimeter

**ELL Strategy** • Understand Context

10.5 *i*Student Edition
10.5 *e*Teacher Edition
Personal Math Trainer
Math on the Spot Video
Animated Math Models
*i*Tools
HMH Mega Math

10.5 Student Edition
10.5 Practice and Homework (in the *Student Edition*)
10.5 Reteach (in the *Chapter Resources*)
10.5 Enrich (in the *Chapter Resources*)
Grab-and-Go™ Centers Kit

**1-2 Days**

**LESSON 10.6**  5.MD.A.1

### Problem Solving • Customary and Metric Conversions . . . . . . 617A

How can you use the strategy *make a table* to help solve problems about customary and metric conversions?

Solve problems about customary and metric conversions using the strategy *make a table*.

**ELL Strategy** • Rephrase

10.6 *i*Student Edition
10.6 *e*Teacher Edition
Personal Math Trainer
Math on the Spot Video
Animated Math Models
*i*Tools
HMH Mega Math

10.6 Student Edition
10.6 Practice and Homework (in the *Student Edition*)
10.6 Reteach (in the *Chapter Resources*)
10.6 Enrich (in the *Chapter Resources*)
Grab-and-Go™ Centers Kit

**Resources** *www.thinkcentral.com*

Interactive Student Edition
Personal Math Trainer

Math on the Spot Video
Animated Math Models

Assessment
HMH Mega Math

*i*Tools

Multimedia *e*Glossary

Professional Development Videos

Real World Videos

# Chapter At A Glance

Domain: **Measurement and Data**

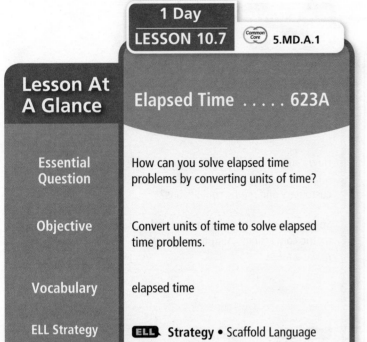

1 Day
LESSON 10.7 5.MD.A.1

## Lesson At A Glance

### Elapsed Time . . . . . 623A

**Essential Question**
How can you solve elapsed time problems by converting units of time?

**Objective**
Convert units of time to solve elapsed time problems.

**Vocabulary**
elapsed time

**ELL Strategy**
 **Strategy** • Scaffold Language

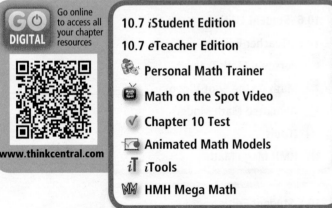

Go online to access all your chapter resources

www.thinkcentral.com

- 10.7 *i*Student Edition
- 10.7 *e*Teacher Edition
- Personal Math Trainer
- Math on the Spot Video
- Chapter 10 Test
- Animated Math Models
- *i*Tools
- HMH Mega Math

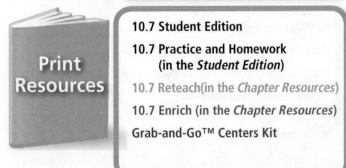

**Print Resources**

- 10.7 Student Edition
- 10.7 Practice and Homework (in the *Student Edition*)
- 10.7 Reteach(in the *Chapter Resources*)
- 10.7 Enrich (in the *Chapter Resources*)
- Grab-and-Go™ Centers Kit

## Teacher Notes

**Assessment**

| Diagnostic | Formative | Summative |
|---|---|---|
| • Show What You Know<br>• Digital Personal Math Trainer | • Lesson Quick Check<br>• Mid-Chapter Checkpoint<br>• Digital Personal Math Trainer<br>- *Assessment Animation*<br>- *Assessment Video* | • Chapter Review/Test<br>• Chapter Test<br>• Performance Assessment Task<br>• Digital Personal Math Trainer |

## Teacher Notes

PROFESSIONAL DEVELOPMENT

# Teaching for Depth

**Matt Larson**
*Curriculum Specialist for Mathematics*
Lincoln Public Schools
Lincoln, Nebraska

## Converting Customary Units

The customary measurement system requires the use of a variety of conversion ratios that are not based on the decimal system. Consequently, students frequently get confused about what operation they should use when making a conversion (Van de Walle, 2004). The following techniques can help students deepen their understanding and lessen their confusion.

- Focus on the meaning of the operations and not just the procedural steps.
- Encourage students to "think" and use common sense. For example, since there are 12 inches in one foot, it is reasonable to have more inches than feet when converting from feet to inches.
- Encourage students to estimate and compare measures after making conversions to check for reasonableness.
- When making multistep conversions, encourage students to tackle the problem as two problems, focusing on only one conversion at a time.

## Capacity vs. Volume

Students often confuse capacity and volume.

- Capacity units are generally applied to liquid measures.
- Since ounces are used for both weight and capacity measures, it is important to refer to fluid ounces (fl oz) when measuring capacity.

### From the Research

"Students should gain facility in expressing measurements in equivalent forms. They use their knowledge of relationships between units and their understanding of multiplicative situations to make conversions ..."
(NCTM, 2000, p. 172)

## Converting Metric Units

Converting metric units is easier than converting customary units because the metric system is related to the decimal system. Emphasizing this connection to the place value system deepens students' understanding. There are two related ways to approach conversions within the metric system that make this connection (Van de Walle, 2004).

- A place-value chart can be used to name the metric units. When using a place-value chart, write the measure to be converted in the column that matches the unit. To convert the unit, write the values in the other columns by applying the ten-to-one relationship as in a place-value chart. When the unit of the measure is changed, the position of the decimal point changes correspondingly.

| kilo- | hecto- | deka- | meter liter gram | deci- | centi- | milli- |
|---|---|---|---|---|---|---|

- Another method to convert metric measures is to multiply or divide by a power of ten. This results in the position of the decimal point changing as with a place-value chart.

## Common Core Mathematical Practices

Converting units of measure within the customary or the metric system provides students an opportunity to **attend to precision.** As they make conversions, they need to check the reasonableness of their results. Students who can apply the techniques on this page will be able to evaluate the reasonableness of their results.

**Professional Development Videos:**
Multiplication and Division: Strategies and Facts, Grades 3–6, Segments 3 and 4

# Daily Classroom Management

## Differentiated Instruction

**Whole Group**

1 ENGAGE

2 EXPLORE

**Small Group**

3 EXPLAIN

 QUICK CHECK

**Whole Group**

4 ELABORATE

5 EVALUATE

**0 to 1 correct**

INTERVENE
These students need lesson support.

**2 correct**

ON LEVEL
These students are ready to begin independent practice.

**Advanced**

ENRICH
These students are ready for enrichment.

### Extra Support

Teachers may need to decelerate the rate at which new material is introduced.

- Reteach (in the *Chapter Resources*)
- ELL Activity

GO DIGITAL

- Strategic Intervention Guide
- Intensive Intervention Guide
- Personal Math Trainer

### On Level

- Practice and Homework (in the *Student Edition*)
- ELL Activity

GO DIGITAL

- HMH Mega Math
- *i*Tools

### Enrich

Teachers may need to accelerate the rate at which new material is introduced.

- Advanced Learners Activity
- Enrich (in the *Chapter Resources*)
- Extend the Project
- ELL Activity

GO DIGITAL

- HMH Mega Math
- *i*Tools

WHAT ARE THE OTHER STUDENTS DOING?

**Differentiated Centers Kit**

The kit provides literature, games, and activities for use every day.

## Strategies for
# English Language Learners

**by Elizabeth Jiménez**
*CEO, GEMAS Consulting*
*Professional Expert on*
*English Learner Education*
*Bilingual Education and Dual Language*
*Pomona, California*

The **Understand Context Strategy** provides a way for teachers to help students understand idioms, colloquial expressions, and words with multiple meanings.

## Benefit to English Language Learners

English Language Learners need explicit instruction on words with idiomatic or multiple meanings because these expressions do not mean what they say—or the meanings shift depending on the context. Native speakers absorb these words as they build their English vocabularies, but idioms and other expressions can frustrate the English Language Learner. Instruction in this area is beneficial to English Language Learners because:

- it clarifies words and phrases that students cannot figure out from cognates.
- it introduces vocabulary that is necessary for comprehension.
- it expands their understanding of English expressions in all subject areas.

### From the Research

"Spanish speakers have trouble knowing what syntactical function English words play, making it difficult for them to use context to determine word meanings. Play, for example, can be a noun, a verb, or an adjective."

(Laura Chris Green, Ph.D. Intercultural Development Research Association Newsletter, 2004.)

## Planning for Instruction

Before starting each lesson, teachers should skim the content, looking for idioms and other expressions that might confuse English Language Learners. Teachers should especially watch for words with different meanings when used as different parts of speech. One example is *pound* as a noun (a pound of meat) and *pound* as a verb. Decide which terms you need to clarify to help students avoid unnecessary frustration as they tackle the math concepts. Teachers can then use the **Frontload Strategy** (introduced in chapter 2) to help students preview a text for words they may not know.

Teachers are looking to assess and then provide support for:

- unfamiliar words or phrases that have multiple-meanings, colloquial expressions, and idiomatic language,
- the language needed for students' concept development, and
- students' prior experiences.

Once teachers have used the Understand Context strategy, they can model how to use a Think Aloud to show how the rest of a sentence or paragraph helps to identify the meaning of a word. Encourage students to offer their own examples of each use of the word, and help with grammar or sentence structure, if needed.

After students have mastered a term, draw their attention to it during lessons. Have them explain its meaning in that context. Encourage them to use the term in their own conversations and explanations.

### Linguistic Note

Help students understand these terms: a *foot* of a body and a *foot* for measurement, a *yard* at a house and a *yard* for measurement, *rules* in school and *rules* in math, and a number *value* and a human *value*, such as honesty.

# Developing Math Language

## Chapter Vocabulary

**capacity** the amount that a container can hold

**decimeter** a metric unit used to measure length or distance; 10 decimeters = 1 meter

**dekameter** a metric unit used to measure length or distance; 10 meters = 1 dekameter

**milligram** a metric unit used to measure mass; 1 milligram = 0.001 gram

**milliliter** a metric unit used to measure capacity; 1 milliliter = 0.001 liter

**weight** how heavy an object is

**Visualize It**
Have students make and complete this chart for each metric measurement word as they go through the chapter.

| Word | |
|---|---|
| Meaning | |
| Example | |

- Interactive Student Edition
- Multimedia eGlossary

## ELL Vocabulary Activity

*See ELL Activity Guide for leveled activities.*

**Objective** Develop vocabulary used in metric measurement.

**Materials** the following prefixes written on index cards: *kilo-*, *hecto-*, *deka-*, *deci-*, *centi-*, *milli-*

Read the cards with students. Remind them that these prefixes tell amounts. Have them work together to put the cards in order from the smallest amount to the largest amount.

Practice vocabulary by using questioning strategies such as:

**Beginning**

- Which is larger, a millimeter or a kilometer? a kilometer

**Intermediate**

- What are three prefixes that name units smaller than 1 meter? deci-, centi-, milli-

**Advanced**

- Explain why multiplication and division are inverse operations. They are opposites; they undo or cancel each other.

## Vocabulary Strategy • Graphic Organizer

**Materials** **K.I.M. Chart** (see *eTeacher Resources*)

- Have students complete a K.I.M. chart graphic organizer. Students choose *meter*, *liter*, or *gram* and write this word in the Key Idea column.
- Then, students fill in the Information column with related vocabulary words to order the units of measure from greatest (*kilo-*) to least (*milli-*).
- Finally, students fill in a Memory Clue for each word (e.g., *kilo-* = 1,000).

| K<br>Key Idea | I<br>Information | M<br>Memory Clue |
|---|---|---|
| | | |

# Review Prerequisite Skills

TIER 2

## Analyze It!

**Objective** Use patterns of zeros to multiply and divide.

Converting from one metric unit to another involves multiplying or dividing by 10, 100, or 1,000. Using two colors, write the problems shown below on the board. Have students state generalizations that can be used to predict the number of zeros in the product or quotient. Possible answers are given.

| | |
|---|---|
| 8 × 1 = 8 | 3,000 ÷ 1 = 3,000 |
| 8 × 10 = 80 | 3,000 ÷ 10 = 300 |
| 8 × 100 = 800 | 3,000 ÷ 100 = 30 |
| 8 × 1,000 = 8,000 | 3,000 ÷ 1,000 = 3 |

When you multiply by 10, 100, or 1,000, the number of zeros in the product is the same as the total number of zeros in the factors.

When you divide by 10, 100, or 1,000, subtract the number of zeros in the divisor from the number of zeros in the dividend to find the number of zeros in the quotient.

TIER 3

## Analyze It!

**Objective** Use patterns of zeros to multiply and divide.

Write these multiplication problems on the board. Ask a student to point to each problem, and have the class respond by holding up fingers to show how many zeros will be in the product.

Write each answer with the appropriate number of zeros, and ask the class to say the answer.

Then have students use their understanding of multiplication patterns of zeros to solve the division problems.

5 × 1 = ☐

5 × 10 = ☐

5 × 100 = ☐

5 × 1,000 = ☐

2,000 ÷ 1 = ☐

2,000 ÷ 10 = ☐

2,000 ÷ 100 = ☐

2,000 ÷ 1,000 = ☐

Have students note that if the product of the basic fact is a multiple of 10, each product in the resulting pattern will include an additional zero.

| | |
|---|---|
| 5 × 6 = 30 | 5 × 600 = 3,000 |
| 5 × 60 = 300 | 5 × 6,000 = 30,000 |

# Measurement and Data

## Common Core Learning Progressions Across the Grades

| In Grade 4, students | In Grade 5, students will | In Grade 6, students will |
|---|---|---|
| • Solve problems involving measurement and conversion of measurements from a larger unit to a smaller unit. | • Convert like measurements within a given measurement system. | • Understand ratio concepts and use ratio reasoning to solve problems.<br>• Use ratio reasoning to convert measurement units. |

## Common Core State Standards Across the Grades

| Before | Grade 5 | After |
|---|---|---|
| Domain: **Measurement and Data**<br>Solve problems involving measurement and conversion of measurements from a larger unit to a smaller unit.<br>**4.MD.A.1** | Domain: **Measurement and Data**<br>Convert like measurement units within a given measurement system.<br>**5.MD.A.1** | Domain: **Ratios and Proportional Relationships**<br>Understand ratio concepts and use ratio reasoning to solve problems.<br>**6.RP.A.3d** |

See A page of each lesson for Common Core Standard text.

Chapter 10

# Introduce the Chapter

## Assessing Prior Knowledge

Use **Show What You Know** to determine if students need intensive or strategic intervention.

Pacing is often used to estimate distances that would otherwise be difficult to measure. In many fictional accounts of buried treasure, the unit used for the treasure maps is a pace.

Ask:

- **How many distances are on the map?** 4 **What unit is used for these distances?** paces **What is the total of the distances?** 26 paces
- **How are paces and feet related?** 2 paces = 5 feet **How can you change paces to feet?** Possible answer: Divide the number of paces by 2 and then multiply by 5.

# Chapter 10 Convert Units of Measure

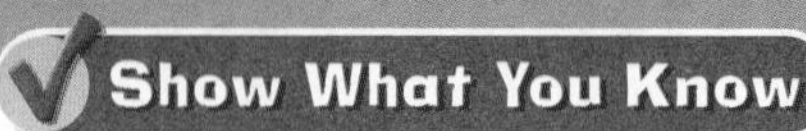

Show What You Know

Personal Math Trainer Online Assessment and Intervention

Check your understanding of important skills.

Name ______

▶ Measure Length to the Nearest Inch

Use an inch ruler. Measure the length to the nearest inch. (3.MD.B.4)

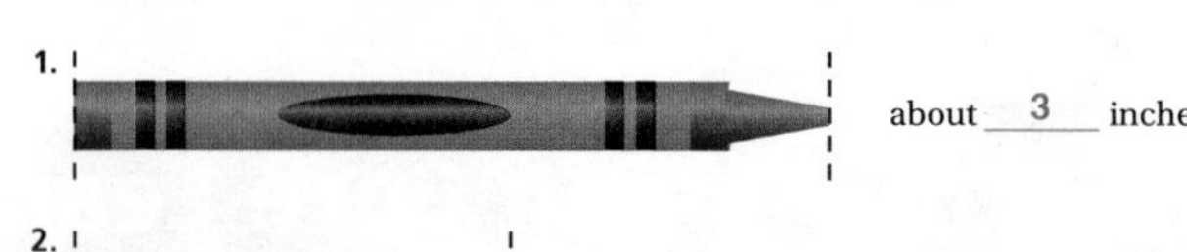

1. about 3 inches

2. about 2 inches

▶ Multiply and Divide by 10, 100, and 1,000 Use mental math. (4.NBT.B.5)

3. $1 \times 5.98 = 5.98$
$10 \times 5.98 = 59.8$
$100 \times 5.98 =$ 598
$1{,}000 \times 5.98 =$ 5,980

4. $235 \div 1 = 235$
$235 \div 10 = 23.5$
$235 \div 100 =$ 2.35
$235 \div 1{,}000 =$ 0.235

▶ Choose Customary Units Write the appropriate unit to measure each. Write *inch, foot, yard,* or *mile.* (4.MD.A.1)

5. length of a pencil inch

6. length of a football field yard

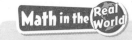

You can step out distances of 5 feet by using an estimate. Two steps or 2 paces is about 5 feet. Act out the directions on the map to find a treasure. About how many feet from start to finish is the path to the treasure?
about 65 feet

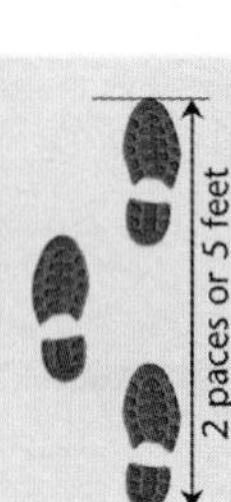

## Show What You Know • Diagnostic Assessment

Use to determine if students need intervention for the chapter's prerequisite skills.

Were students successful with Show What You Know?

If NO...then INTERVENE

If YES...then use INDEPENDENT ACTIVITIES

| | Skill | Missed More Than | Personal Math Trainer | Intervene With |
|---|---|---|---|---|
| TIER 3 | Measure Length to the Nearest Inch | 0 | 3.MD.B.4 | *Intensive Intervention* Skill 51; *Intensive Intervention User Guide* Activity 10 |
| TIER 2 | Multiply and Divide by 10, 100, and 1,000 | 0 | 4.NBT.B.5 | *Strategic Intervention* Skill 24 |
| TIER 2 | Choose Customary Units | 0 | 4.MD.A.1 | *Strategic Intervention* Skill 13 |

Differentiated Centers Kit

Use the Enrich Activity in the *Chapter Resources* or the independent activities in the *Grab-and-Go™ Differentiated Centers Kit.*

## Vocabulary Builder

▶ Visualize It

**Sort the review and preview words into the Venn diagram.**

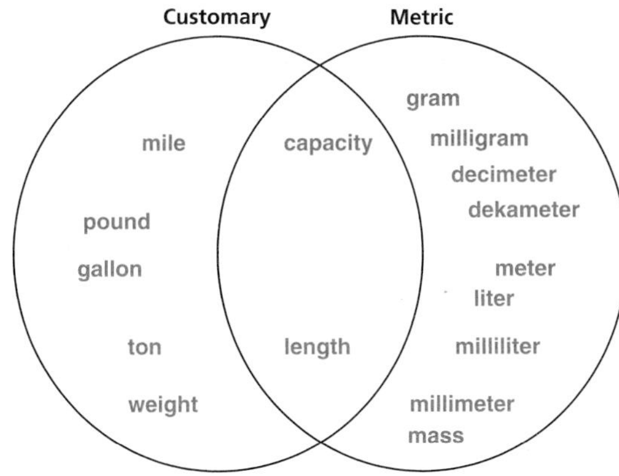


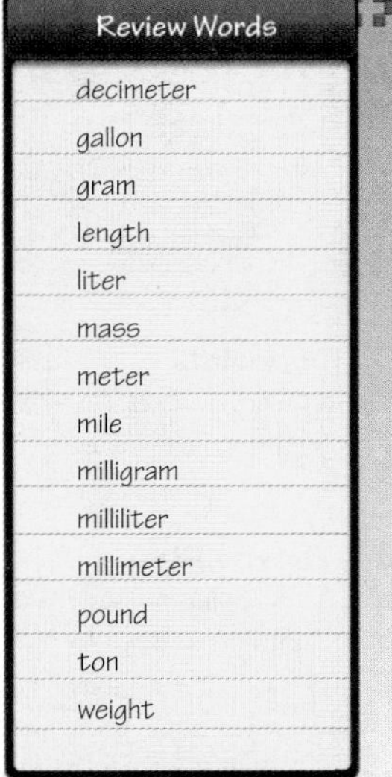

Review Words
decimeter
gallon
gram
length
liter
mass
meter
mile
milligram
milliliter
millimeter
pound
ton
weight


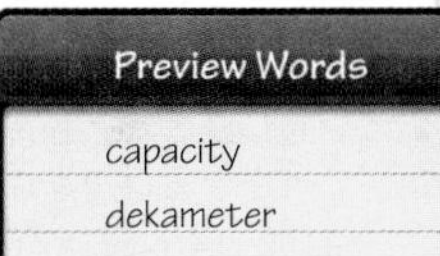


▶ Understand Vocabulary

**Complete the sentences.**

1. A metric unit of length that is equal to one tenth of a meter is a __decimeter__.
2. A metric unit of length that is equal to one thousandth of a meter is a __millimeter__.
3. A metric unit of capacity that is equal to one thousandth of a liter is a __milliliter__.
4. A metric unit of length that is equal to 10 meters is a __dekameter__.
5. A metric unit of mass that is equal to one thousandth of a gram is a __milligram__.

## Vocabulary Builder

Have students complete the activities on this page by working alone or with partners.

### ▶ Visualize It

A Venn diagram shows relationships between sets of things. Words relating to customary measurement should be placed in the left portion of the left circle. Words relating to metric measurement should be placed in the right portion of the right circle. The words *capacity* and *length* are placed within the intersecting portion because they relate to both customary and metric measurement.

### ▶ Understand Vocabulary

Students can enhance their understanding on key chapter vocabulary through the use of the vocabulary cards found in the Student Edition. Have students cut out the cards and create their own deck of terms. You can use these cards to reinforce knowledge and reading across the content areas.

**School-Home Letter** available in English and Spanish, in the *Chapter Resources*. Multiple languages available online at *www.thinkcentral.com*

# Intervention Options RtI Response to Intervention

**Use Show What You Know, Lesson Quick Check, and Assessments to diagnose students' intervention levels.**

### TIER 1

#### On-Level Intervention

For students who are generally at grade level but need early intervention with the lesson concepts, use:

- **Reteach (in the *Chapter Resources*)**

 **Personal Math Trainer**

 **Tier 1 Activity online**

### TIER 2

#### Strategic Intervention

For students who need small group instruction to review concepts and skills needed for the chapter, use:

 **Strategic Intervention Guide**

 **Personal Math Trainer**

 **Prerequisite Skills Activities**

 **Tier 2 Activity online**

### TIER 3

#### Intensive Intervention

For students who need one-on-one instruction to build foundational skills for the chapter, use:

 **Intensive Intervention Guide**

 **Personal Math Trainer**

 **Prerequisite Skills Activities**

### ENRICHMENT

#### Independent Activities

For students who successfully complete lessons, use:

**Differentiated Centers Kit**

- **Advanced Learners Activity for every lesson**
- **Enrich Activity (in the *Chapter Resources*)**

 **HMH Mega Math**

## Chapter 10 Vocabulary Game

# Going Places with GO Math Words

## Introduce the Words

Provide these student-friendly explanations of chapter vocabulary. Ask volunteers to explain the math term in their own words.

- **The amount a container can hold is called its *capacity*.**
- **10 meters is equal to 1 *dekameter*, which is almost 33 feet.**
- **10 centimeters is equal to 1 *decimeter*, which is almost 4 inches.**
- **The amount of matter in an object is its *mass*.**
- **A *milligram (mg)* is $\frac{1}{1000}$ of a gram.**
- **A *milliliter (mL)* is about 20 drops or $\frac{1}{5}$ of a teaspoon of liquid.**

## Math Journal WRITE Math

Have students draw pictures or use numbers to show what each term means. Then ask them to discuss their work with a partner.

## Bingo:

### Play the Game

eTeacher Resources

The game may be played before, during, or after the content is taught. Read the game directions with students. Divide them into groups, and have each group choose a student to be the caller. Explain that the caller chooses a word card, reads the definition, and then puts the card in a second pile. Have each group play until a player marks 5 boxes in a row going down, across, or diagonally and calls "Bingo." Ask the caller to check the definitions read as the winner reads the words.

The directions for playing the game can also be found in the Chapter Resource book.

**ELL** Discuss any game terms to ensure that students understand their meanings.

Going Places with GO MATH! Words

# Bingo

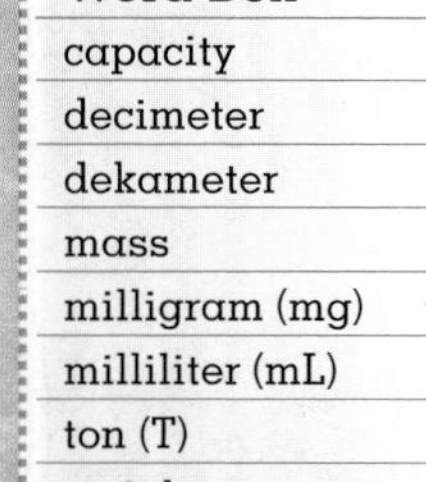

| Word Box |
|---|
| capacity |
| decimeter |
| dekameter |
| mass |
| milligram (mg) |
| milliliter (mL) |
| ton (T) |
| weight |

For 3–6 players

**Materials**

- 1 set of word cards
- 1 Bingo board for each player
- game markers

**How to Play**

1. The caller chooses a card and reads the definition. Then the caller puts the card in a second pile.
2. Players put a marker on the word that matches the definition each time they find it on their Bingo boards.
3. Repeat Steps 1 and 2 until a player marks 5 boxes in a line going down, across, or on a slant and calls "Bingo."

- To check the answers, the player who said "Bingo" reads the words aloud while the caller checks the definitions.

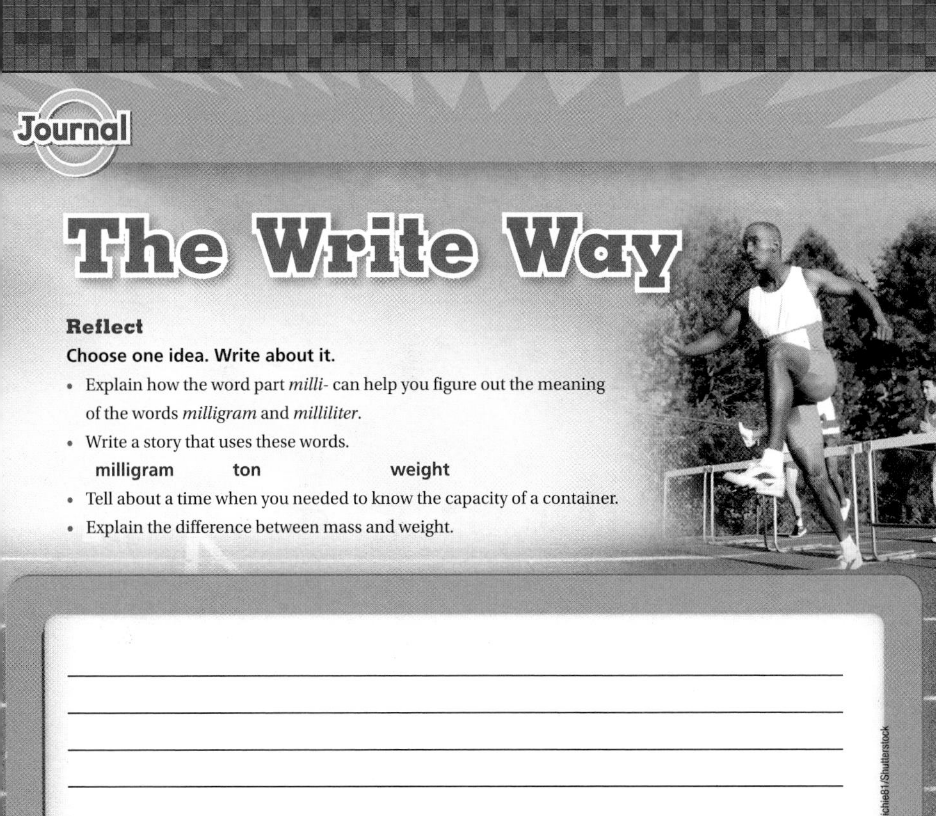

Journal

# The Write Way

**Reflect**

**Choose one idea. Write about it.**

- Explain how the word part *milli-* can help you figure out the meaning of the words *milligram* and *milliliter*.
- Write a story that uses these words.
  **milligram** **ton** **weight**
- Tell about a time when you needed to know the capacity of a container.
- Explain the difference between mass and weight.



584B

## What You Need

Each group of players needs one set of the Vocabulary Cards in the Student Edition.

Each player needs one copy of the Bingo board on *eTeacher Resources* p. **TR155** and about 10–15 game markers. Have each player write the vocabulary words from this chapter in random order in the boxes on the Bingo board. Point out that they will write each word more than once.

## The Write Way

These short, informal writing activities address the vocabulary and content from this chapter. Communicating about math clarifies and deepens students' understandings about math concepts.

Read the writing prompts with students. Give them 5–10 minutes to choose an idea and write about it.

When students have completed their first drafts, share and discuss the following questions. Then provide students with additional time to use the questions to review and revise their writing.

- **Does my writing show that I understand the math idea(s)?**
- **Do I use math vocabulary correctly?**
- **Is my writing clear and easy to follow?**
- **Do I use complete sentences? Have I checked to be sure my grammar, spelling, and punctuation are correct?**

Ask volunteers to share their finished writing with a partner or the class. Encourage discussion of different ways students may have addressed each prompt. Point out that often there is not just one correct answer.

**ELL** Have students use the Vocabulary Cards in the Student Edition as a reference for word meanings. Guide them to use the lessons and example problems in the Student Edition if they need additional support.

LESSON 10.1

# Customary Length

FOCUS COHERENCE RIGOR

## LESSON AT A GLANCE

### FCR Focus:

**Common Core State Standards**

**5.MD.A.1** Convert among different-sized standard measurement units within a given measurement system (e.g., convert 5 cm to 0.05 m), and use these conversions in solving multi-step, real world problems.

**MATHEMATICAL PRACTICES**

**MP5** Use appropriate tools strategically. **MP7** Look for and make use of structure.

### FCR Coherence:

**Standards Across the Grades**

| Before | Grade 5 | After |
|---|---|---|
| 4.MD.A.1 | 5.MD.A.1 | 6.RP.A.3d |

### FCR Rigor:

**Level 1: Understand Concepts**....................*Share and Show* (Checked Items)

**Level 2: Procedural Skills and Fluency**.......*On Your Own*

**Level 3: Applications**...............................*Think Smarter and Go Deeper*

### Learning Objective

Compare, contrast, and convert customary units of length.

### Language Objective

Students work in small teams to practice and explain how you can compare and convert customary units of length.

### Materials

MathBoard

FCR For more about how *GO Math!* fosters **Coherence** within the Content Standards and Mathematical Progressions for this chapter, see page 583J.

## About the Math

**Professional Development**

### Why Teach This

Converting and comparing units of customary length is not only a math skill, but an everyday life skill. Students are likely to find many opportunities in their lives to use the skills learned in this lesson. The equivalence relationships students will work with include:

| Customary Units of Length |
|---|
| 1 foot (ft) = 12 inches (in.) |
| 1 yard (yd) = 3 feet |
| 1 mile (mi) = 5,280 feet |
| 1 mile = 1,760 yards |

To convert units of length, students should continue to reinforce the importance of the generalization that we use multiplication to change a larger unit of length to a smaller unit of length and division to change a smaller unit of length to a larger unit of length.

Professional Development Videos

Interactive Student Edition

Personal Math Trainer

Math on the Spot

Animated Math Models

*i*Tools: Measurement

HMH Mega Math

## Problem of the Day 10.1

Which addition property is being used in this problem? Commutative Property

$$1\frac{3}{4} + 2\frac{5}{7} = 2\frac{5}{7} + 1\frac{3}{4}$$

### Vocabulary

- Interactive Student Edition
- Multimedia eGlossary

## Fluency Builder

**Multiply** Write the product as a mixed number.

1. $7 \times 1\frac{4}{5}$ $12\frac{3}{5}$
2. $4 \times 2\frac{3}{8}$ $9\frac{4}{8}$ or $9\frac{1}{2}$
3. $2 \times 3\frac{1}{6}$ $6\frac{2}{6}$ or $6\frac{1}{3}$
4. $3 \times 4\frac{2}{5}$ $13\frac{1}{5}$
5. $6 \times 4\frac{3}{4}$ $28\frac{2}{4}$ or $28\frac{1}{2}$
6. $2 \times 8\frac{1}{3}$ $16\frac{2}{3}$

# 1 ENGAGE

with the Interactive Student Edition

## Essential Question

How can you compare and convert customary units of length?

## Making Connections

Invite students to tell you what they know about distances.

**About how far do you live from school? What is the farthest distance you have ever walked? About how far is the distance from your house to a friend's house?**

## Learning Activity

What is the problem the students are trying to solve? Connect the story to the problem.

- **What does Jed want to find out?** the distance between where he and Ramona live
- **How far does Cagney live from Jed?** 3 miles
- **How does Ramona measure the distance between Jed's house and her house?** in yards

## Literacy and Mathematics

Choose one or more of the following activities.

- Have students write and perform a brief skit in which walking or traveling a certain distance is a main feature of the story.
- Write the word *close* on the board. Review the comparative and superlative forms *closer* and *closest* with students and have them illustrate or define the terms. Then have them use each word in a sentence.

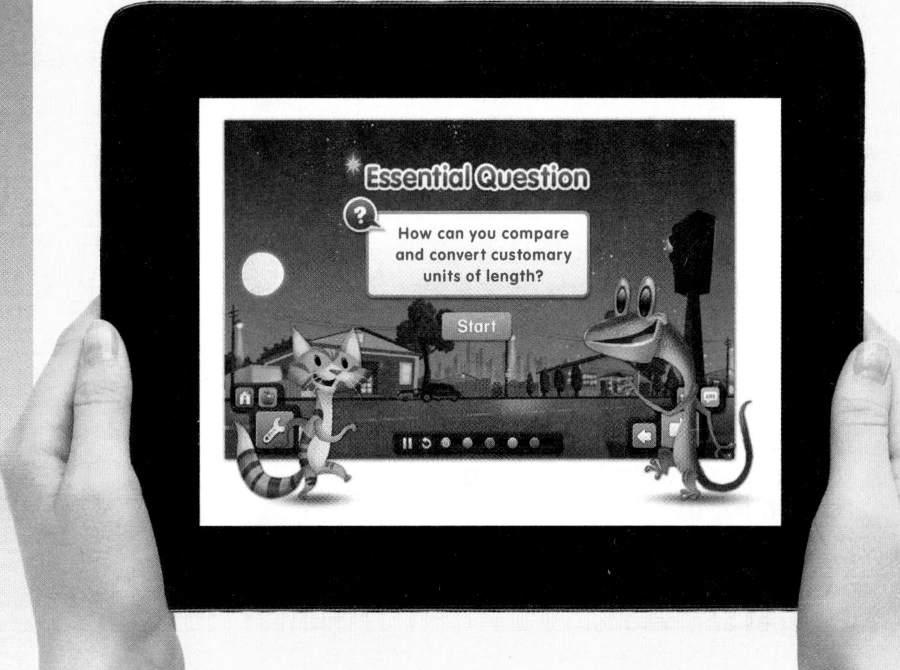

# 2 EXPLORE

Common Core **5.MD.A.1** Convert among different-sized standard measurement units within a given measurement system (e.g., convert 5 cm to 0.05m), and use these conversions in solving multi-step, real world problems.

## Unlock the Problem

Common Core MATHEMATICAL PRACTICES

Read the scenario and discuss the diagram that shows 1 yard and 3 feet are equivalent measures.

**MP5 Use appropriate tools strategically.** As students use the bar model to write an equation to find the answer, ask:

- **What does each unit in the model represent?** Each unit in the model represents 3 feet.
- **How many yards is each unit in the bar model? Explain your answer.** Each unit in the bar represents 1 yard because 3 feet = 1 yard.

After students solve the problem, ask:

- **What operation is represented by the bar model? Explain your answer.** Division; possible explanation: 24 feet was the whole or dividend, and 3 was the divisor or number in each group. To find the number of groups, we divided 24 by 3.

Have students note that in this example, division is used to change a smaller unit (feet) to a larger unit (yards).

**MP7 Look for and make use of structure.**

- **What is the relationship between the number of feet and the number of yards? How do you know?** There are 3 times as many feet as yards. I know because there are 3 feet in every yard.

**Math Talk** Use **Math Talk** to focus on students' understanding of using multiplication and division to convert customary units of length.

- **What operation would you use to convert yards into feet? Why?** multiplication; Each yard is made up of 3 feet, so to find the number of feet I combine equal groups of 3, which is multiplication.

## ELL Strategy: Rephrase

Read the problem to students: **Katie has 5 yards of ribbon. She needs only 4 feet to finish trimming her costume. How much ribbon will be left?**

- Have partners write down the units given and then rephrase the problem to each other. Invite a volunteer to rephrase the problem for the class.
- After solving the problem, pairs should compare and discuss their solution strategies and results. 15 feet − 4 feet = 11 feet

---

Name ______________________

Lesson 10.1

### Customary Length

**Essential Question** How can you compare and convert customary units of length?

Measurement and Data—5.MD.A.1
MATHEMATICAL PRACTICES
MP5, MP7

### Unlock the Problem (Real World)

To build a new swing, Mr. Mattson needs 9 feet of rope for each side of the swing and 6 more feet for the monkey bar. The hardware store sells rope by the yard.

- How many feet of rope does Mr. Mattson need for the swing? $9 + 9 = 18$ feet
- How many feet does Mr. Mattson need for the swing and the monkey bar combined? $18 + 6 = 24$ feet

Mr. Mattson needs to find how many yards of rope he needs to buy. He will need to convert 24 feet to yards. How many groups of 3 feet are in 24 feet?

| A 12-inch ruler is 1 foot. | | |
|---|---|---|
| A yardstick is 1 yard. | | |

3 feet = 1 yard

**Use a bar model to write an equation.**

MODEL: 8; 3 … 3; 24

RECORD:

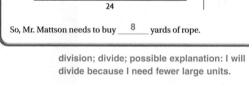

| total feet | | feet in 1 yard | | total yards |
|---|---|---|---|---|
| ↓ | | ↓ | | ↓ |
| 24 | ÷ | 3 | = | 8 |

So, Mr. Mattson needs to buy 8 yards of rope.

**Math Talk** MATHEMATICAL PRACTICES 6 What operation did you use when you found groups of 3 feet in 24 feet? Do you multiply or divide when you convert a smaller unit to a larger unit? Explain.

division; divide; possible explanation: I will divide because I need fewer large units.



Chapter 10 585

---

### Reteach 10.1 (RtI)

Name ______________________ Lesson 10.1 Reteach

**Customary Length**

You can convert one customary unit of length to another customary unit of length by multiplying or dividing.

Multiply to change from larger to smaller units of length.

Divide to change from smaller to larger units of length.

**Customary Units of Length**
1 foot (ft) = 12 inches (in.)
1 yard (yd) = 3 feet
1 mile (mi) = 5,280 feet
1 mile = 1,760 yards

**Convert 3 feet to inches.**

| Step 1 | Step 2 | Step 3 |
|---|---|---|
| Decide: (Multiply) or Divide<br>feet → inches<br>larger → smaller | Think:<br>1 ft = 12 in., so<br>3 ft = (3 × 12) in. | Multiply.<br>3 × 12 = 36 |

So, 3 feet = 36 inches.

**Convert 363 feet to yards.**

| Step 1 | Step 2 | Step 3 |
|---|---|---|
| Decide: Multiply or (Divide)<br>feet → yards<br>smaller → larger | Think:<br>3 ft = 1 yd,<br>so 363 ft = (363 ÷ 3) yd. | Divide.<br>363 ÷ 3 = 121 |

So, 363 feet = 121 yards.

**Convert.**

1. 33 yd = 99 ft
2. 300 mi = 528,000 yd
3. 46 in. = 3 ft 10 in.
4. 96 yd = 288 ft
5. 48 ft = 16 yd
6. 2 mi 20 yd = 3,540 yd

**Compare. Write <, >, or =.**

7. 2 yd (<) 7 ft
8. 67 mi (=) 117,920 yd
9. 250 yd (<) 800 ft
10. 14 yd 2 ft (>) 16 ft
11. 34 ft 10 in. (<) 518 in.
12. 5 mi 8 ft (>) 8,800 yd

Chapter Resources 10-5 Reteach


### Enrich 10.1 — Differentiated Instruction

Name ______________________ Lesson 10.1 Enrich

**Customary Length Measurements Match**

**Convert each measurement. Write the letter of the correct measure.**

**Customary Units of Length**
1 foot (ft) = 12 inches (in.)
1 yard (yd) = 3 ft
1 mile (mi) = 5,280 ft
1 mi = 1,760 yd

| | | |
|---|---|---|
| 1. | 28 yd = F ft | A. 3 |
| 2. | 372 in. = H yd 1 ft | B. 346 |
| 3. | J yd = 18 ft | C. 44 |
| 4. | B in. = 28 ft 10 in. | D. 65 |
| 5. | 132 ft = C yd | E. 180 |
| 6. | 780 in. = D ft | F. 84 |
| 7. | I yd = 219 ft | G. 12,520 |
| 8. | E in. = 15 ft | H. 10 |
| 9. | 15,840 ft = A mi | I. 73 |
| 10. | 7 mi 200 yd = G yd | J. 6 |

11. **Stretch Your Thinking** Niko rides his bike 5,300 yards to his friend's house. About how many miles does Niko ride?
1,760 yd = 1 mi
5,300 yards is about 3 miles.

12. **Write Math** **Explain** how you found your answer for Exercise 11.
Possible answer: I estimated. There are about 1,800 yards in 1 mile, 3,600 yards in 2 miles, and 5,400 yards in 3 miles.

Chapter Resources 10-6 Enrich

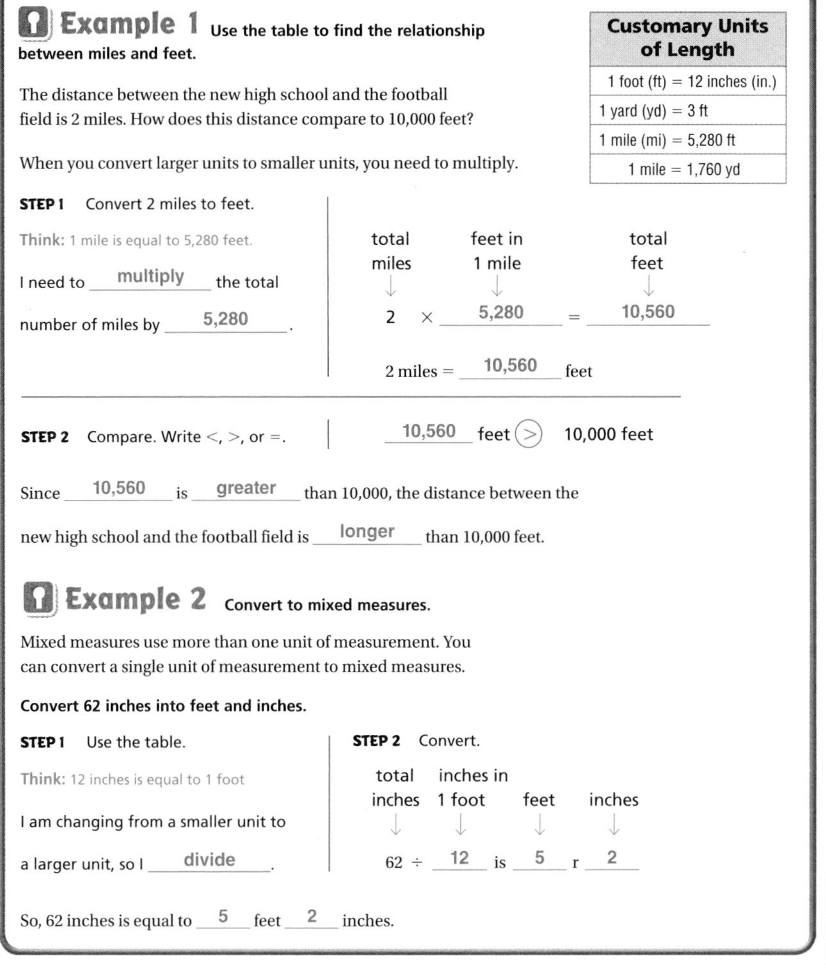

## Example 1 Use the table to find the relationship between miles and feet.

| Customary Units of Length |
|---|
| 1 foot (ft) = 12 inches (in.) |
| 1 yard (yd) = 3 ft |
| 1 mile (mi) = 5,280 ft |
| 1 mile = 1,760 yd |

The distance between the new high school and the football field is 2 miles. How does this distance compare to 10,000 feet?

When you convert larger units to smaller units, you need to multiply.

**STEP 1** Convert 2 miles to feet.

Think: 1 mile is equal to 5,280 feet.

I need to multiply the total number of miles by 5,280.

total miles ↓ 2 × feet in 1 mile ↓ 5,280 = total feet ↓ 10,560

2 miles = 10,560 feet

**STEP 2** Compare. Write <, >, or =.

10,560 feet > 10,000 feet

Since 10,560 is greater than 10,000, the distance between the new high school and the football field is longer than 10,000 feet.

## Example 2 Convert to mixed measures.

Mixed measures use more than one unit of measurement. You can convert a single unit of measurement to mixed measures.

**Convert 62 inches into feet and inches.**

**STEP 1** Use the table.

Think: 12 inches is equal to 1 foot

I am changing from a smaller unit to a larger unit, so I divide.

**STEP 2** Convert.

total inches ↓ 62 ÷ inches in 1 foot ↓ 12 is feet ↓ 5 r inches ↓ 2

So, 62 inches is equal to 5 feet 2 inches.

- MATHEMATICAL PRACTICE 6 **Explain** how to convert the mixed measures, 12 yards 2 feet, to a single unit of measurement in feet. How many feet is it?

Possible explanation: Multiply 12 yards by 3 to get 36 feet and then add the 2 feet; 38 feet.





## Advanced Learners

Interpersonal
Individual / Partners

**Materials** almanacs, Internet, sports reference books

- **In American football, yards are used to measure the distance a team moves up and down a field. Suppose a receiver ran 55 yards. How many feet would the receiver have run?** 165 feet
- Have students use almanacs, Internet, or sports reference books to write three conversion problems like the one above.
- Ask students to write an explanatory sentence about the sport they have written about to help others understand the situation.
- Have students trade problems and solve.
- You may choose to include some of these problems on assessments for the entire class.

## Example 1

Discuss the scenario.

- **The units in this problem are miles and feet. Which is the smaller unit? Which is the larger unit? Explain how you know.** The smaller unit is feet and the larger unit is miles. Possible answer: Miles is the larger unit, because 1 mile is made up of 5,280 smaller equal parts called feet.

## Example 2

- **The mixed measures in Steps 1 and 2 are feet and inches. Which is the smaller unit? Which is the larger unit? Explain how you know.** The smaller unit is inches and the larger unit is feet. Possible answer: Feet is the larger unit, because 1 foot is made up of 12 smaller equal parts called inches.

**MP6 Attend to precision.** Check that students understand that to add measurements they must be in the same units; therefore, 12 yards must be converted to feet before it is added to 2 feet.

**GO DEEPER**

When converting units of length, ask students to suggest reasons why we use multiplication to change a larger unit to a smaller unit and division to change a smaller unit to a larger unit. It is important for students to conclude that changing larger units to smaller units represents an *increase* in the number of units, and changing smaller units to larger units represents a *decrease* in the number of units. We use multiplication to increase the number of units and division to decrease the number of units.

You may want to give students additional experience in converting customary linear units by using an activity found in *i*Tools: Measurement • Equivalent Measures • Length. *i*Tools can be found *at www.thinkcentral.com.*

## COMMON ERRORS

**Error** Students choose the wrong operation to convert.

**Example**

6 ft = 18 yd

**Springboard to Learning** Given two units of length, make sure students can identify the smaller unit and the larger unit. Then ask them to record the generalization shown below and refer to it as needed.

- To change a smaller unit to a larger unit, divide.
- To change a larger unit to a smaller unit, multiply.

## 3 EXPLAIN

### Share and Show 

The first problem connects to the learning model. Have students use the MathBoard to explain their thinking.

Use **Math Talk** to focus on students' understanding of converting customary units.

- **If you aren't sure whether to multiply, how could drawing a bar model help you decide?** The bar model could show you whether you are increasing the number of units or decreasing them. If you are increasing them, you multiply.

Use the checked exercises for **Quick Check**. Students should show their answers for the Quick Check on the MathBoard.

### Quick Check

a student misses the checked exercises

**Differentiate Instruction** with
- Reteach 10.1
- Personal Math Trainer 5.MD.A.1
- RtI Tier 1 Activity (online)

### On Your Own

For Exercises 7–9, make sure students understand the meaning of the inequality symbols, < and >.

**THINK SMARTER**

This item assesses a student's ability to convert among customary units of length, specifically feet to yards. A student who chooses *multiply* by 3 may have memorized the conversion factor, but does not understand the relative magnitude of units of measure and has chosen the incorrect operation. A student who chooses addition or subtraction as the operation may not understand the basic concept of conversion. A student who chooses the wrong number in the second box may not know the customary length equivalents.

---

Name ______________________

### Share and Show (MATH BOARD)

**Convert.**

1. 2 mi = 3,520 yd
2. 6 yd = 18 ft
3. 90 in. = 7 ft 6 in.

Possible explanation: I know I should multiply if I am converting to a smaller unit, because there will be more of the smaller units.

Math Talk — MATHEMATICAL PRACTICES 1
Make Sense of Problems
How do you know when to multiply to convert a measurement?

### On Your Own

**Practice: Copy and Solve** Convert.

4. 125 in. = ■ ft ■ in. 10; 5
5. 46 ft = ■ yd ■ ft 15; 1
6. 42 yd 2 ft = ■ ft 128

**Compare. Write <, >, or =.**

7. 8 ft (<) 3 yd
8. 2 mi (>) 10,500 ft
9. 3 yd 2 ft (=) 132 in.

10. GO DEEPER Terry is making 6 hat and scarf sets. Each scarf requires 2 yards of material and each hat requires 18 inches of material. How many feet of material does he need for all 6 hat and scarf sets?

45 feet of material

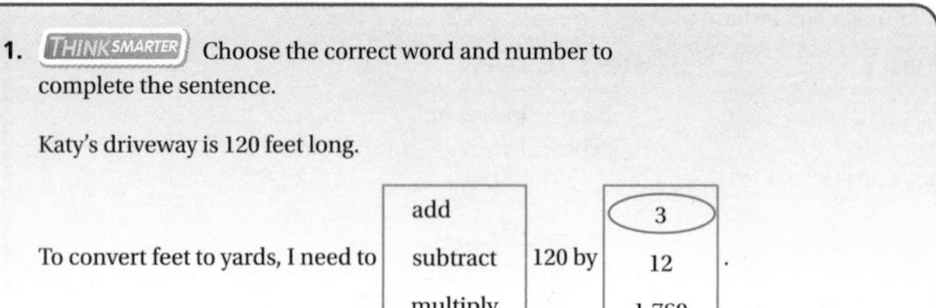

11. THINK SMARTER Choose the correct word and number to complete the sentence.

Katy's driveway is 120 feet long.

To convert feet to yards, I need to [add / subtract / multiply / **divide** (circled)] 120 by [**3** (circled) / 12 / 1,760 / 5,280].

## Problem Solving • Applications 

12. GO DEEPER Javon is helping his dad build a tree house. He has a piece of trim that is 13 feet long. How many pieces can Javon cut that are 1 yard long? How much of a yard will he have left over?

4 pieces; $\frac{1}{3}$ yard

13. THINK SMARTER Patty is building a rope ladder for a tree house. She needs two 5-foot pieces of rope for the sides of the ladder. She needs 7 pieces of rope, each 18 inches long, for the steps. How many feet of rope does Patty need to make the ladder? Write your answer as a mixed number and as a mixed measure in feet and inches.

$20\frac{1}{2}$ feet; 20 feet 6 inches

### Connect to Reading

**Compare and Contrast**

When you compare and contrast, you tell how two or more things are alike and different. You can compare and contrast information in a table.

Complete the table below. Use the table to answer the questions.

| Linear Units | | | | |
|---|---|---|---|---|
| Yards | 1 | 2 | 3 | 4 |
| Feet | 3 | 6 | 9 | 12 |
| Inches | 36 | 72 | 108 | 144 |

14. MATHEMATICAL PRACTICE 7 **Identify Relationships** How are the items in the table alike? How are they different?

Possible answer: They are all units of customary length, but each is a different-sized unit.

15. MATHEMATICAL PRACTICE 7 **Look for a Pattern** What do you notice about the relationship between the number of larger units and the number of smaller units as the length increases? Explain.

Possible explanation: The larger units increase by only a small amount, but the smaller units increase by a greater amount.

## DIFFERENTIATED INSTRUCTION INDEPENDENT ACTIVITIES

### Differentiated Centers Kit

***Activities***
***Size It Up Metric!***

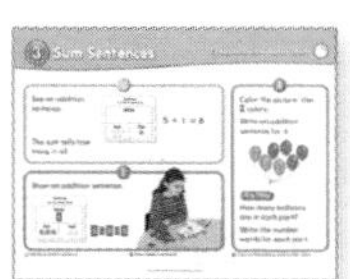

Students complete orange Activity Card 2 by estimating and then measuring the length in metric units.

***Literature***
***A Math Mix-Up***

Students read about a mix-up in customary and metric measurements that led to the NASA's Mars Climate Orbiter crashing into Mars.

***Games***
***2 Steps Forward, 1 Step Back***

Students convert customary and metric units to move along the game path.

# 4 ELABORATE

## Problem Solving • Applications

MATHEMATICAL PRACTICES

GO DEEPER

To solve Problem 12, some students may find it helpful if you point out that "trim" is a decorative wood strip.

THINK SMARTER

### Math on the Spot Video Tutor

Use this video to help students model and solve this type of *Think Smarter* problem.

**Math on the Spot** videos are in the Interactive Student Edition and at *www.thinkcentral.com*.

## Connect to Reading

Work cooperatively as a class to complete the activity.

# 5 EVALUATE Formative Assessment

## Essential Question

### Using the Language Objective

**Reflect** Have students work in small teams to practice and explain to answer the essential question.

**How can you compare and convert customary units of length?** Possible answer: First, I use division to convert the smaller unit to the larger unit, or I use multiplication to convert the larger unit to the smaller unit. Then, I use a <, >, or = symbol to compare.

## Math Journal WRITE Math

**Explain how to compare two lengths that are measured in different-sized units.**

## Practice and Homework

Use the Practice and Homework pages to provide students with more practice of the concepts and skills presented in this lesson. Students master their understanding as they complete practice items and then challenge their critical thinking skills with Problem Solving. Use the Write Math section to determine student's understanding of content for this lesson. Encourage students to use their Math Journals to record their answers.

Name ________________

**Customary Length**

**Practice and Homework**
**Lesson 10.1**

Common Core **COMMON CORE STANDARD—5.MD.A.1** *Convert like measurement units within a given measurement system.*

**Convert.**

1. 12 yd = 36 ft

total yards → 12 × feet in 1 yard → 3 = total feet → 36

12 yards = 36 feet

2. 5 ft = 60 in.

3. 5 mi = 26,400 ft

4. 240 in. = 20 ft

5. 100 yd = 300 ft

6. 10 ft = 120 in.

7. 150 in. = 12 ft 6 in.

8. 7 yd 2 ft = 23 ft

9. 10 mi = 52,800 ft

**Compare. Write <, >, or =.**

10. 23 in. < 2 ft

11. 25 yd = 75 ft

12. 6,200 ft > 1 mi 900 ft

13. 100 in. < 3 yd 1 ft

14. 1,000 ft > 300 yd

15. 500 in. > 40 ft

### Problem Solving (Real World)

16. Marita orders 12 yards of material to make banners. If she needs 1 foot of fabric for each banner, how many banners can she make?

36 banners

17. Christy bought an 8-foot piece of lumber to trim a bookshelf. Altogether, she needs 100 inches of lumber for the trim. Did Christy buy enough lumber? Explain.

No. She bought only 96 inches of trim.

18. WRITE Math Explain how to compare two lengths that are measured in different-sized units.

Check students' explanations.





## Cross-Curricular

### SCIENCE

- A *force* is a push or pull that causes an object to move, stop, or change direction. Different forces act on a race car to make it move, speed up, and turn as it drives around the track.
- In 2010, Dario Franchitti won the Indy 500 with a race speed of over 160 miles per hour. The race is 500 miles long. What is the length of the race in yards? 880,000 yards

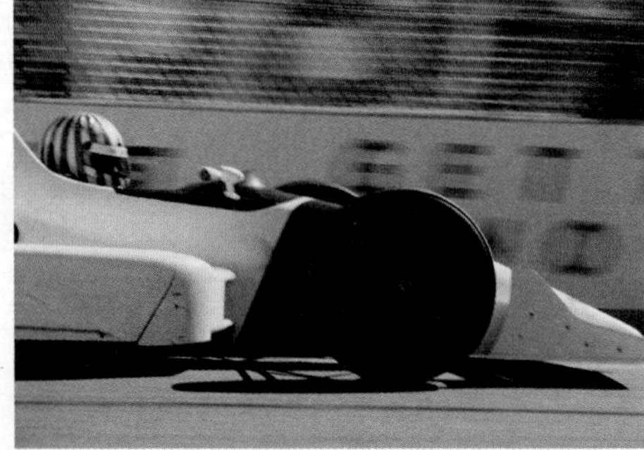

### SOCIAL STUDIES

- Construction on the Panama Canal began in 1904, when Theodore Roosevelt was president. The Panama Canal connects the Atlantic and Pacific oceans and links American ports on the Atlantic coast with those on the Pacific coast to allow for more efficient trade routes. The canal is 50 miles long between the deep waters of both oceans.
- How many feet long is the Panama Canal from the deep waters of the Atlantic to the deep waters of the Pacific? 264,000 feet

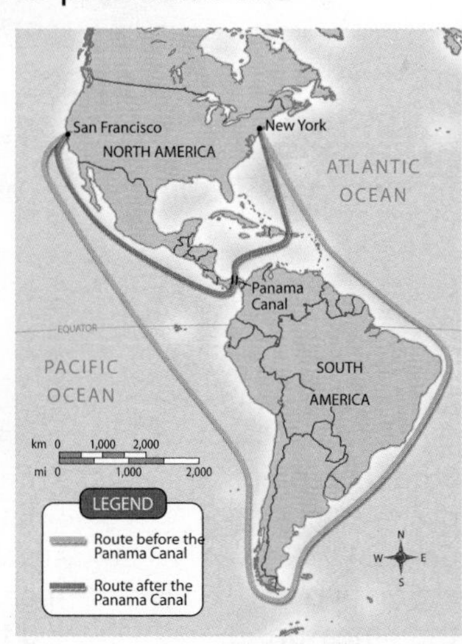

## Lesson Check (5.MD.A.1)

1. Jenna's garden is 5 yards long. How long is her garden in feet?

   15 feet

2. Ellen needs to buy 180 inches of ribbon to wrap a large present. The store sells ribbon only in whole yards. How many yards does Ellen need to buy to have enough ribbon?

   5 yards

## Spiral Review (5.OA.B.3, 5.NF.B.6, 5.NF.B.4a)

3. McKenzie works for a catering company. She is making iced tea for an upcoming event. For each container of tea, she uses 16 tea bags and 3 cups of sugar. If McKenzie uses 64 tea bags, how many cups of sugar will she use?

   12 cups

4. Javier bought 48 sports cards at a yard sale. Of the cards, $\frac{3}{8}$ were baseball cards. How many cards were baseball cards?

   18 cards

5. What is the quotient of 396 divided by 12?

   33

6. What is the unknown number in Sequence 2 in the chart? What rule can you write that relates Sequence 2 to Sequence 1?

| Sequence Number | 1 | 2 | 3 | 8 | 10 |
|---|---|---|---|---|---|
| Sequence 1 | 4 | 8 | 12 | 32 | 40 |
| Sequence 2 | 8 | 16 | 24 | 64 | ? |

   80; Multiply by 2.



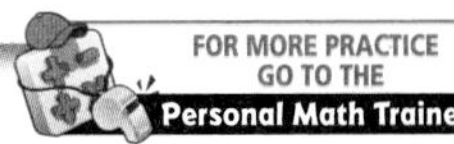




Continue concepts and skills practice with Lesson Check. Use Spiral Review to engage students in previously taught concepts and to promote content retention. Common Core standards are correlated to each section.

LESSON 10.2

# Customary Capacity

FOCUS COHERENCE RIGOR

## LESSON AT A GLANCE

### F C R Focus:

**Common Core State Standards**

**5.MD.A.1** Convert among different-sized standard measurement units within a given measurement system (e.g., convert 5 cm to 0.05 m), and use these conversions in solving multi-step, real world problems.

**MATHEMATICAL PRACTICES**

**MP5** Use appropriate tools strategically.
**MP6** Attend to precision.

### F C R Coherence:

**Standards Across the Grades**

| **Before** | **Grade 5** | **After** |
|---|---|---|
| 4.MD.A.1 | 5.MD.A.1 | 6.RP.A.3d |

### F C R Rigor:

**Level 1:** Understand Concepts.................... *Share and Show* (✓ Checked Items)
**Level 2:** Procedural Skills and Fluency....... *On Your Own*
**Level 3:** Applications................................ *Think Smarter and Go Deeper*

### Learning Objective

Compare, contrast, and convert customary units of capacity.

### Language Objective

Students list some customary units of capacity and work with a partner to explain how you can compare and convert customary units of capacity.

### Materials

MathBoard

F C R For more about how *GO Math!* fosters **Coherence** within the Content Standards and Mathematical Progressions for this chapter, see page 583J.

## About the Math

**Professional Development**

### Why Teach This

Converting and comparing units of customary capacity is an everyday life skill. Students will work with these equivalence relationships:

| Customary Units of Capacity |
|---|
| 1 cup (c) = 8 fluid ounces (fl oz) |
| 1 pint (pt) = 2 cups |
| 1 quart (qt) = 2 pints |
| 1 gallon (gal) = 4 quarts |

Students should continue to reinforce the importance of the generalization that we use multiplication to change a larger unit of capacity to a smaller unit of capacity and division to change a smaller unit of capacity to a larger unit of capacity.

Professional Development Videos

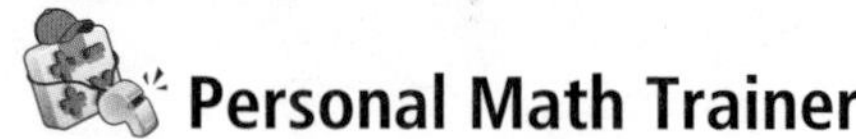

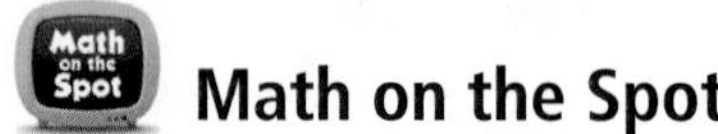

*i*Tools: Measurement

HMH Mega Math

## Daily Routines

Common Core

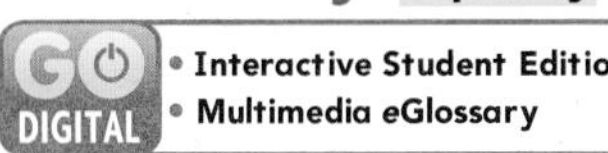

### Problem of the Day 10.2

Mr. Ferguson purchased 12 feet of border to trim a bulletin board in his classroom. How many yards of border did Mr. Ferguson purchase? 4 yards

**Vocabulary** capacity

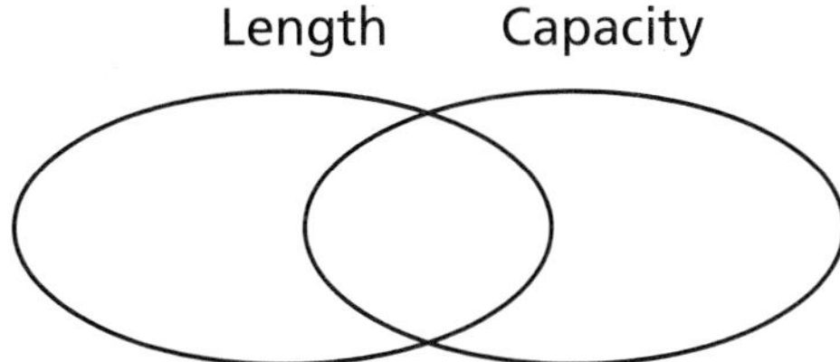


### Vocabulary Builder

**Length and Capacity** Draw and label two intersecting ovals, as shown below.

Length Capacity

Use the graphic to discuss with students properties that length has but capacity does not (e.g., it measures distance), that capacity has but length does not (e.g., it measures liquid volume), and that the two have in common (e.g., you use the same method to convert from a larger unit to a smaller unit).

### Literature Connection

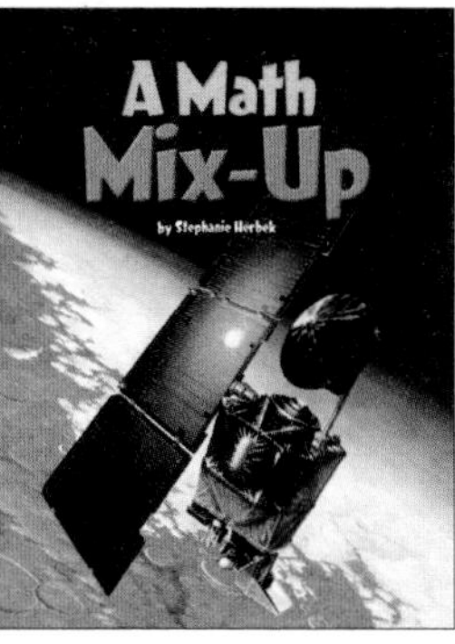

*A Math Mix-Up*

**From the Grab-and-Go™ Differentiated Centers Kit**

Students will read about a mix-up in customary and metric measurements that led to the NASA's Mars Climate Orbiter crashing into Mars.

# 1 ENGAGE

## with the Interactive Student Edition

### Essential Question

How can you compare and convert customary units of capacity?

### Making Connections

Invite students to tell you what they know about units of capacity.

**What units of capacity do you know?** gallon, pint, liter, quart, etc.
**What items are sold in pints and quarts?** milk, ice cream, yogurt, berries, etc.

### Learning Activity

What is the problem the students are trying to solve? Connect the story to the problem.

- **What problem is Jed trying to solve?** how many pints of strawberries the neighbor picked
- **How many quarts of strawberries did the neighbor pick?** 2 quarts
- **How many pints of strawberries are used for each bowl of fruit salad?** 1 pint
- **What do you know about pints and quarts?** Possible answer: Pints are less than quarts.

### Literacy and Mathematics

Choose one or more of the following activities.

- Have students write a real or imagined story about a time they have gone fruit picking. Have them describe how much fruit they picked and what they did with the fruit.
- Write the words *compare* and *convert* on the board and underline the prefixes *com-* and *con-*. Explain that the prefixes mean "with." Elicit words with the prefixes *com-/con-* from students (*converse, connect, compare, combine*) and have them discuss their meaning with a partner. Have them use each word in a sentence.

# 2 EXPLORE

## Unlock the Problem

MATHEMATICAL PRACTICES

**Do you know how to convert cups to fluid ounces? Read and solve the problem to learn the answer.**

Discuss the problem. Make sure students understand that the term *fluid ounces* refers to a liquid measure in a capacity context, and it is different than the term *ounces*, which is a measure of the weight of an object (such as the weight of a package in pounds and ounces).

**MP5 Use appropriate tools strategically.** As students use the bar model to convert cups to fluid ounces, ask:

- **What does each unit in the bar represent?** Each unit in the bar represents 8 fluid ounces.
- **Why do you use the bar model to write a multiplication equation to find the number of fluid ounces?** Possible answer: Since I am changing larger units (cups) to smaller units (fluid ounces), the number of units will increase. Multiplication by a whole number is used to increase the number of units.

**MP6 Attend to precision.** Is there more than one way to compare 7 cups and 64 fluid ounces? Explain. Yes; You can either convert cups to fluid ounces and compare, or you can convert fluid ounces to cups and compare.

## ELL Strategy: Understand Context

Write *can* and *punch* on the board and read the words aloud with students.

- **Both of these words have two different meanings.** Demonstrate the meanings in context. Show or draw the examples to clarify meaning.
  **You *can* do math problems.**
  **Paint comes in a *can*.**
  **You drink *punch*.**
  **You *punch* a hole in a card.**
- Have volunteers offer sentences using both meanings of *can*. Repeat with *punch*.

**5.MD.A.1** Convert among different-sized standard measurement units within a given measurement system (e.g., convert 5 cm to 0.05m), and use these conversions in solving multi-step, real world problems.

Lesson 10.2

Name ____________

## Customary Capacity

**Essential Question** How can you compare and convert customary units of capacity?

**Measurement and Data—5.MD.A.1**
**MATHEMATICAL PRACTICES**
**MP5, MP6**

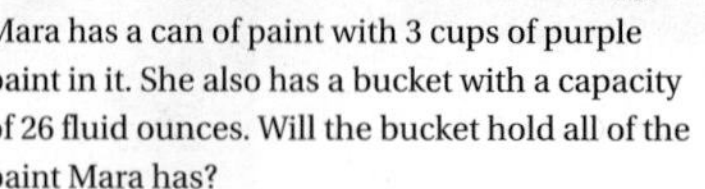


Mara has a can of paint with 3 cups of purple paint in it. She also has a bucket with a capacity of 26 fluid ounces. Will the bucket hold all of the paint Mara has?

- What capacity does Mara need to convert? 3 cups to fluid ounces
- After Mara converts the units, what does she need to do next? Compare the amount of paint with the fluid ounces the bucket will hold.

The **capacity** of a container is the amount the container can hold.

1 cup (c) = 8 fluid ounces (fl oz)

**Use a bar model to write an equation.**

**STEP 1** Convert 3 cups to fluid ounces.

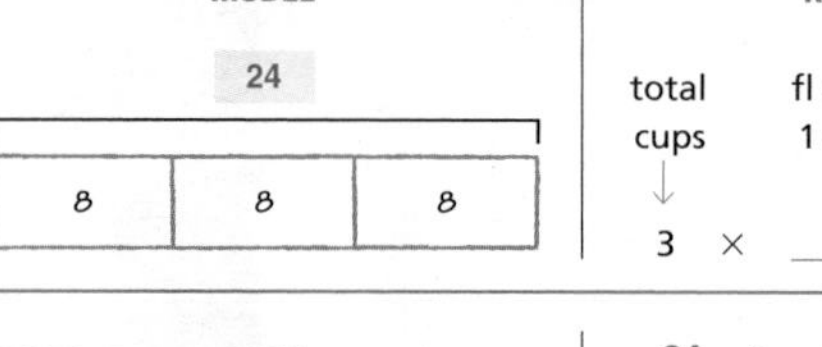

| MODEL | RECORD |
|---|---|
| 24: [8][8][8] | total cups ↓ 3 × fl oz in 1 cup ↓ 8 = total fl oz ↓ 24 |

**STEP 2** Compare. Write <, >, or =. 24 fl oz < 26 fl oz

Since 24 fluid ounces is less than 26 fluid ounces, Mara's bucket will hold all of the paint.

- MATHEMATICAL PRACTICE 6 What if Mara has 7 cups of green paint and a container filled with 64 fluid ounces of yellow paint? Which color paint does Mara have more of? **Explain** your reasoning.
  Mara has more yellow paint. Possible explanation: There are 7 cups, or 7 × 8 = 56 fluid ounces of green paint. Since 64 > 56, Mara has more yellow paint.





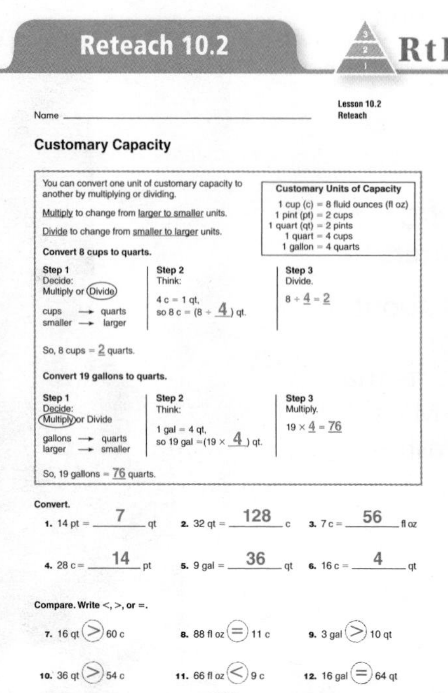

Reteach 10.2 RtI

Name ____________ Lesson 10.2 Reteach

### Customary Capacity

You can convert one unit of customary capacity to another by multiplying or dividing.

Multiply to change from larger to smaller units.

Divide to change from smaller to larger units.

| Customary Units of Capacity |
|---|
| 1 cup (c) = 8 fluid ounces (fl oz) |
| 1 pint (pt) = 2 cups |
| 1 quart (qt) = 2 pints |
| 1 quart = 4 cups |
| 1 gallon = 4 quarts |

**Convert 8 cups to quarts.**

| Step 1 | Step 2 | Step 3 |
|---|---|---|
| Decide: Multiply or (Divide). cups → quarts; smaller → larger | Think: 4 c = 1 qt, so 8 c = (8 ÷ 4) qt. | Divide. 8 ÷ 4 = 2 |

So, 8 cups = 2 quarts.

**Convert 19 gallons to quarts.**

| Step 1 | Step 2 | Step 3 |
|---|---|---|
| Decide: (Multiply) or Divide. gallons → quarts; larger → smaller | Think: 1 gal = 4 qt, so 19 gal = (19 × 4) qt. | Multiply. 19 × 4 = 76 |

So, 19 gallons = 76 quarts.

**Convert.**

1. 14 pt = 7 qt
2. 32 qt = 128 c
3. 7 c = 56 fl oz
4. 28 c = 14 pt
5. 9 gal = 36 qt
6. 16 c = 4 qt

**Compare. Write <, >, or =.**

7. 16 qt > 60 c
8. 88 fl oz = 11 c
9. 3 gal > 10 qt
10. 36 qt > 54 c
11. 66 fl oz < 9 c
12. 16 gal = 64 qt

Chapter Resources 10-7 Reteach
© Houghton Mifflin Harcourt Publishing Company

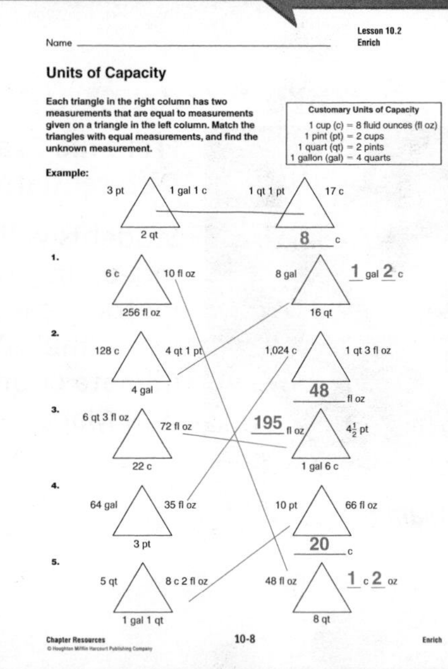

Enrich 10.2 Differentiated Instruction

Name ____________ Lesson 10.2 Enrich

### Units of Capacity

**Each triangle in the right column has two measurements that are equal to measurements given on a triangle in the left column. Match the triangles with equal measurements, and find the unknown measurement.**

| Customary Units of Capacity |
|---|
| 1 cup (c) = 8 fluid ounces (fl oz) |
| 1 pint (pt) = 2 cups |
| 1 quart (qt) = 2 pints |
| 1 gallon (gal) = 4 quarts |

**Example:** 3 pt, 1 gal 1 c, 2 qt — 1 qt 1 pt, 17 c, 8 c

| |  |  |
|---|---|---|
| 1. | 6 c, 10 fl oz, 256 fl oz | 8 gal, 1 gal 2 c, 16 qt |
| 2. | 128 c, 4 qt 1 pt, 4 gal | 1,024 c, 1 qt 3 fl oz, 48 fl oz |
| 3. | 6 qt 3 fl oz, 72 fl oz, 22 c | 195 fl oz, $4\frac{1}{2}$ pt, 1 gal 6 c |
| 4. | 64 gal, 35 fl oz, 3 pt | 10 pt, 66 fl oz, 20 c |
| 5. | 5 qt, 8 c 2 fl oz, 1 gal 1 qt | 48 fl oz, 1 c 2 oz, 8 qt |

Chapter Resources 10-8 Enrich
© Houghton Mifflin Harcourt Publishing Company

## 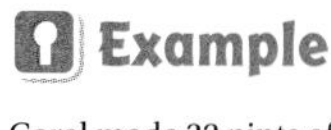 Example

Coral made 32 pints of fruit punch for a party. She needs to carry the punch in 1-gallon containers. How many containers does Coral need?

| Customary Units of Capacity |
|---|
| 1 cup (c) = 8 fluid ounces (fl oz) |
| 1 pint (pt) = 2 cups |
| 1 quart (qt) = 2 pints |
| 1 gallon (gal) = 4 quarts |

To convert a smaller unit to a larger unit, you need to divide. Sometimes you may need to convert more than once.

**Convert 32 pints to gallons.**

**STEP 1** Write an equation to convert pints to quarts.

total pints ÷ pints in 1 qt = total quarts

32 ÷ 2 = 16

**STEP 2** Write an equation to convert quarts to gallons.

total quarts ÷ quarts in 1 gal = total gallons

16 ÷ 4 = 4

So, Coral needs 4 1-gallon containers to carry the punch.

## Share and Show 

1. Use the picture to complete the statements and convert 3 quarts to pints.

   a. 1 quart = 2 pints

   b. 1 quart is greater than 1 pint.

   c. 3 qt × 2 pt in 1 qt = 6 pt

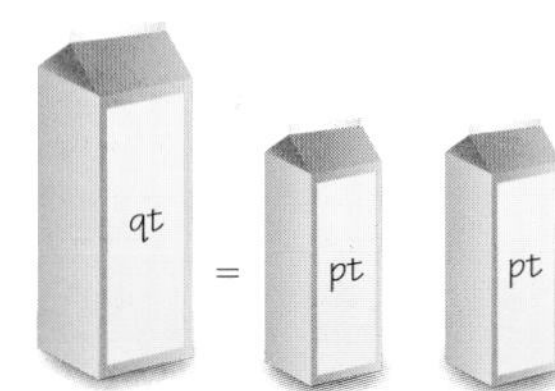


**Convert.**

2. 3 gal = 24 pt

3. 5 qt = 10 pt

4. 6 qt = 24 c

Possible explanation: Converting the two types of units is similar because I need to divide when converting smaller units to larger ones and multiply when I convert larger units to smaller ones. It is different because I use different numbers of units in the conversions.

MATHEMATICAL PRACTICES 2

Reason Abstractly Explain how converting units of capacity is similar to converting units of length. How is it different?





## Advanced Learners

Visual
Individual

- For Exercises 8–13 on page 593, have students make a table of ordered pairs, like the one below, for two units of measure. The table does not need to include the numbers used in the exercises.
- Students graph the relationship between the two units, and draw a line through the points.
- Have students use the ordered pairs from the completed graphs to complete the conversion exercises.

| Cups | 1 | 2 | 4 | 6 | 8 | 10 |
|---|---|---|---|---|---|---|
| Fl oz | 8 | 16 | 32 | 48 | 64 | 80 |

## Example

- **Why is division used in each step of the solution?** In each step, we are changing a smaller unit to a larger unit, so the number of units will decrease in each step. Division by a whole number is used to decrease the number of units.

# 3 EXPLAIN

## Share and Show 

The first problem connects to the learning model. Have students use the MathBoard to explain their thinking.

Use the checked exercises for **Quick Check**. Students should show their answers for the Quick Check on the MathBoard.

Use **Math Talk** to focus on students' understanding of conversion concepts.

Draw students' attention to the process of converting capacity and the process of converting length.

##  Quick Check 

**If** a student misses the checked exercises

**Then** Differentiate Instruction with
- Reteach 10.2
- Personal Math Trainer 5.MD.A.1
- RtI Tier 1 Activity (online)

##  COMMON ERRORS

**Error** Students use division to change a larger unit to a smaller unit.

**Example**

2 quarts = 1 pint

**Springboard to Learning** In the example, have students identify which unit is larger and which unit is smaller. Then ask: Will the larger unit have a greater number or a smaller number of units? Students should realize the larger unit should have fewer units to equal the smaller unit.

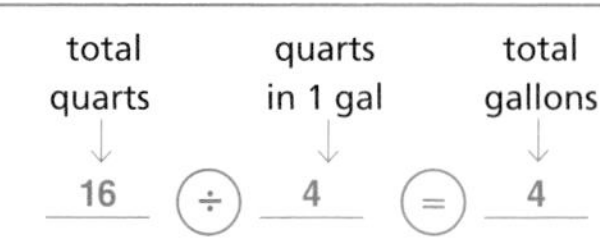
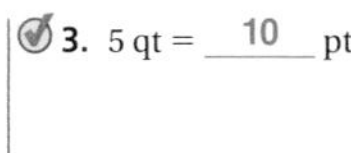
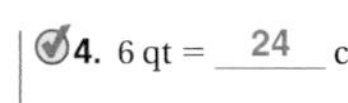

## On Your Own

To complete the exercises, encourage students to refer to the equivalent customary relationships shown in the table on page 592.

For Exercise 20, give students an opportunity to make a tally of how many students used mental math for each of Exercises 14–19.

- **For which exercise did the greatest number of students use mental math?**
- **For which exercise did the least number of students use mental math?**

Refer students to Exercise 21.

- **To solve the problem, you perform two steps to convert pints to fluid ounces. What would we need to know to complete the conversion using only one step?** the number of fluid ounces in 1 pint
- **One pint is the same as what number of cups?** 1 pint = 2 cups
- **Explain how you would use the relationship 1 pint = 2 cups to solve the problem using only one step.** Possible answer: Since there are 8 fluid ounces in 1 cup and 2 cups in 1 pint, there are 2 × 8, or 16 fluid ounces in 1 pint. Multiply the number of pints by 16 to find the number of fluid ounces.

You may want to give students additional experience in converting units of capacity using the activity found in *i*Tools: Measurement • Equivalent Measures • Capacity. *i*Tools can be found at *www.thinkcentral.com.*

Name ____________________

### On Your Own

**Convert.**

**5.** 38 c = 19 pt

**6.** 36 qt = 9 gal

**7.** 104 fl oz = 13 c

**Practice: Copy and Solve** **Convert.**

**8.** 200 c = ■ qt 50

**9.** 22 pt = ■ fl oz 352

**10.** 8 gal = ■ qt 32

**11.** 72 fl oz = ■ c 9

**12.** 2 gal = ■ pt 16

**13.** 48 pt = ■ gal 6

**Compare. Write <, >, or =.**

**14.** 28 c (=) 14 pt

**15.** 25 pt (<) 13 qt

**16.** 20 qt (=) 80 c

**17.** 12 gal (<) 50 qt

**18.** 320 fl oz (>) 18 pt

**19.** 15 qt (<) 63 c

**20.** WRITE Math Which of exercises 14–19 could you solve mentally? Explain your answer for one exercise.

Possible answer: I could solve exercise 14 mentally. Possible explanation: I can multiply 14 and 2 to change pints to cups for comparison; 28 c = 28 c.

**21.** GO DEEPER Larry made 4 batches of punch. Each batch uses 16 fluid ounces of lemon juice and 3 pints of orange juice. If each serving is 1 cup, how many servings did he make all together?

32 servings

 MATHEMATICAL PRACTICES ANALYZE • LOOK FOR STRUCTURE • PRECISION

## Problem Solving • Applications 

**Show your work. For 22–24, use the table.**

**22.** MATHEMATICAL PRACTICE 4 **Use Graphs** Complete the table, and make a graph showing the relationship between quarts and pints.

| Quarts | 0 | 1 | 2 | 3 | 4 |
|---|---|---|---|---|---|
| Pints | 0 | 2 | 4 | 6 | 8 |

Quarts-Pints Relationship

Pints: 0 1 2 3 4 5 6 7 8 9 10

Quarts: 0 1 2 3 4 5 6 7 8 9 10

**23.** GO DEEPER Describe any pattern you notice in the pairs of numbers you graphed. Write a rule to describe the pattern.

Possible description: The number of pints is double the number of quarts. I can use the rule, multiply the number of quarts by 2 to find the number of pints.

**24.** THINK SMARTER What other pair of customary units of capacity have the same relationship as pints and quarts? Explain.

pints and cups; Possible explanation: There are 2 pints in 1 quart and there are 2 cups in 1 pint.

**25.** THINK SMARTER Shelby made 5 quarts of juice for a picnic. She said that she made $1\frac{1}{4}$ cups of juice. Explain Shelby's mistake.

Possible answer: Shelby divided the number of quarts by 4 to convert to cups. She should have multiplied the number of quarts by 4 to find the number of cups in 5 quarts. $5 \times 4 = 20$ cups

## DIFFERENTIATED INSTRUCTION | INDEPENDENT ACTIVITIES

**Differentiated Centers Kit**

***Literature***
***A Math Mix-Up***

Students read about a mix-up in customary and metric measurements that led to the NASA's Mars Climate Orbiter crashing into Mars.

***Games***
***2 Steps Forward, 1 Step Back***

Students convert customary and metric units to move along the game path.

# 4 ELABORATE

## Problem Solving • Applications 

MATHEMATICAL PRACTICES

**MP4 Model with mathematics.**
Problem 22 requires students to represent a linear relationship graphically.

THINK SMARTER

### Math on the Spot Video Tutor

Use this video to help students model and solve this type of *Think Smarter* problem.

**Math on the Spot** videos are in the Interactive Student Edition and at *www.thinkcentral.com*.

THINK SMARTER

Item 25 assesses a student's ability to convert among customary units of capacity. This item requires the student to find and explain an error in converting quarts to cups. To do so, students must analyze, verify, or correct the reasoning of others. A student that answers this problem incorrectly may be able to convert quarts to cups but may not be able to understand how the number of quarts was incorrectly converted to cups. Some students may be able to use the concept of size to answer the problem. These students may recognize that Shelby's statement is incorrect because a quart is larger than a cup, and the number of cups should be more than the number of quarts.

# 5 EVALUATE Formative Assessment

## Essential Question

### Using the Language Objective

**Reflect** Have students list some customary units of capacity and work with a partner to answer the essential question.

**How can you compare and convert customary units of capacity?** Possible answer: First, I use division to convert the smaller unit to the larger unit, or I use multiplication to convert the larger unit to the smaller unit. Then, I use a <, =, or > symbol to compare.

## Math Journal WRITE Math

**Give some examples of when you would measure capacity in each of the units of capacity shown in the table on page 592.**

## Practice and Homework

Use the Practice and Homework pages to provide students with more practice of the concepts and skills presented in this lesson. Students master their understanding as they complete practice items and then challenge their critical thinking skills with Problem Solving. Use the Write Math section to determine student's understanding of content for this lesson. Encourage students to use their Math Journals to record their answers.

Name ______

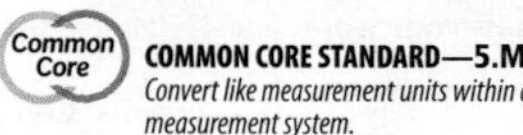


### Customary Capacity

Common Core **COMMON CORE STANDARD—5.MD.A.1** *Convert like measurement units within a given measurement system.*

**Convert.**

1. 5 gal = 40 pt
   Think: 1 gallon = 4 quarts
   1 quart = 2 pints
2. 192 fl oz = 12 pt
3. 15 pt = 30 c
4. 240 fl oz = 30 c
5. 32 qt = 8 gal
6. 10 qt = 40 c
7. 48 c = 12 qt
8. 72 pt = 9 gal
9. 128 fl oz = 8 pt

**Compare. Write <, >, or =.**

10. 17 qt (>) 4 gal
11. 96 fl oz (<) 8 pt
12. 400 pt (<) 100 gal
13. 100 fl oz (<) 16 pt
14. 74 fl oz (>) 8 c
15. 12 c (=) 3 qt

### Problem Solving Real World

16. Vickie made a recipe for 144 fluid ounces of scented candle wax. How many 1-cup candle molds can she fill with the recipe?

    18 candle molds

17. A recipe calls for 32 fluid ounces of heavy cream. How many 1-pint containers of heavy cream are needed to make the recipe?

    2 pints

18. **WRITE** Math Give some examples of when you would measure capacity in each of the units of capacity shown in the table on page 592.

    Check students' examples.

## Lesson Check (5.MD.A.1)

1. Rosa made 12 gallons of lemonade to sell at a lemonade stand. How many pints of lemonade did she make?

   96 pints

2. Ebonae's fish tank holds 40 gallons. How many quarts does the fish tank hold?

   160 quarts

## Spiral Review (5.NBT.B.5, 5.NF.A.1, 5.NF.B.3, 5.MD.A.1)

3. A mountain climber climbed 15,840 feet on her way to the summit of a mountain. How many miles did she climb?

   3 miles

4. Jamal is making blueberry muffins. He has $6\frac{3}{4}$ cups of batter, but he needs a total of 12 cups. How much more batter does Jamal need?

   $5\frac{1}{4}$ cups

5. At a building site, there are 16 pallets with sacks of cement. The total weight of all the pallets and cement is 4,856 pounds. Each pallet with cement weighs the same amount. How much does each pallet with cement weigh?

   $303\frac{1}{2}$ pounds

6. A publisher shipped 15 boxes of books to a bookstore. Each box contained 32 books. How many books did the publisher ship to the bookstore?

   480 books

Continue concepts and skills practice with Lesson Check. Use Spiral Review to engage students in previously taught concepts and to promote content retention. Common Core standards are correlated to each section.

LESSON 10.3

# Weight

## LESSON AT A GLANCE

FOCUS COHERENCE RIGOR

### F C R Focus:

**Common Core State Standards**

**5.MD.A.1** Convert among different-sized standard measurement units within a given measurement system (e.g., convert 5 cm to 0.05 m), and use these conversions in solving multi-step, real world problems.

**MATHEMATICAL PRACTICES**

**MP1** Make sense of problems and persevere in solving them.
**MP6** Attend to precision.

### F C R Coherence:

**Standards Across the Grades**

| Before | Grade 5 | After |
|---|---|---|
| 4.MD.A.1 | 5.MD.A.1 | 6.RP.A.3d |

### F C R Rigor:

**Level 1:** Understand Concepts....................*Share and Show* (✓ Checked Items)
**Level 2:** Procedural Skills and Fluency.......*On Your Own*
**Level 3:** Applications.................................*Think Smarter and Go Deeper*

### Learning Objective

Compare, contrast, and convert customary units of weight.

### Language Objective

Students draw and label in their Math Journal the process for how you can compare and convert customary units of weight.

### Materials

MathBoard

F C R For more about how *GO Math!* fosters **Coherence** within the Content Standards and Mathematical Progressions for this chapter, see page 583J.

## About the Math

Professional Development

### Why Teach This

Converting and comparing units of customary weight is not only a math skill, but an everyday life skill. Students are likely to find many opportunities in their lives to use the skills learned in this lesson. The equivalence relationships students will work with include:

| Customary Units of Weight |
|---|
| 1 pound (lb) = 16 ounces (oz) |
| 1 ton (T) = 2,000 pounds |

To convert units of weight, students should continue to reinforce the importance of the generalization that we use multiplication to change a larger unit of weight to a smaller unit of weight and division to change a smaller unit of weight to a larger unit of weight.

 Professional Development Videos

 Interactive Student Edition

 Personal Math Trainer

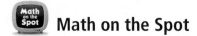

 Math on the Spot

 Animated Math Models

*i*T *i*Tools: Measurement

 HMH Mega Math

## Daily Routines

**Common Core**

### Problem of the Day 10.3

Mara made lemonade for the school picnic. She made 8 quarts of lemonade. How many gallons of lemonade did Mara make?
2 gallons

### Vocabulary

- Interactive Student Edition
- Multimedia eGlossary

### Fluency Builder

**Mental Math** Review the mental math strategy *use a double* to find products.

Find $6 \times 8$.
Use $3 \times 8$, since 3 doubled is 6.
$3 \times 8 = 24$; 24 doubled is 48. So, $6 \times 8$ is 48.

Find the products.

1. $11 \times 11$ 121
   $22 \times 11$ 242
2. $12 \times 9$ 108
   $12 \times 18$ 216
3. $13 \times 2$ 26
   $13 \times 4$ 52
   $13 \times 8$ 104
   $13 \times 16$ 208

# 1 ENGAGE

## with the Interactive Student Edition

### Essential Question

How can you compare and convert customary units of weight?

### Making Connections

Invite students to tell you what they know about units of weight.

**What units of weight do you know?** ounces, grams, pounds, tons, etc. **What kinds of real-world objects are sold by weight?** fish, meat, cheese, etc.

### Learning Activity

What is the problem the students are trying to solve? Connect the story to the problem.

- **What does Jed want to know?** how the weights of the garden hoe and the chair compare
- **How much does the garden hoe weigh?** 35 ounces
- **How much does the chair weigh?** 9 pounds
- **How do the weights of these objects compare to the weights of other objects you know?** Answers will vary.

### Literacy and Mathematics

Choose one or more of the following activities.

- Ask students to discuss in writing how the problem would change if the chair weighed 5 pounds, and the garden hoe weighed 50 ounces.
- Write the word *weight* on the board and underline the *–ei-* vowel combination. Pronounce the word for students and have them repeat it. Elicit other words from students that have the long a sound, that are spelled with *–ei- (eight, freight, sleigh, neigh)*.

Common Core **5.MD.A.1** Convert among different-sized standard measurement units within a given measurement system (e.g., convert 5 cm to 0.05m), and use these conversions in solving multi-step, real world problems.

# 2 EXPLORE

## Unlock the Problem (Real World)

Common Core MATHEMATICAL PRACTICES

To introduce the lesson, have students watch the Real World Video.

**MP1 Make sense of problems and persevere in solving them.** Discuss the scenario. Point out to students how the bar model helps them visualize the problem.

- **How can you compare the 62-ounce and 4-pound weights?** Possible answer: We need to express the weights using the same unit.

**MP6 Attend to precision**

- **Why is multiplication used to find the number of ounces?** Possible answer: Since we are changing larger units (pounds) to smaller units (ounces), the number of units will increase.

Math Talk Use **Math Talk** to focus on students' understanding of choosing the correct operation when converting between units.

- **If you accidentally divided instead of multiplied to convert pounds to ounces, how might you realize that your answer is unreasonable?** Possible answer: It doesn't make sense to have less of a smaller unit equal more of a larger unit.

GO DEEPER

Have students work in pairs to create a problem involving ounces and pounds that would need to be solved using division. Have them justify division as the correct operation.

## ELL Strategy:

### Identify Relationships

Write these customary units of weight on the board:

16 ounces = 1 pound   2,000 pounds = 1 ton

- Help students see that a ton is much heavier than a pound and a pound is heavier than an ounce.
- **Should we measure the weight of a truck in pounds or tons?** tons **If a truck weighs 2 tons, how many pounds does it weigh?** 4,000 lbs
- **Should we measure the weight of a book in pounds or tons?** pounds **If a book weighs 3 pounds, how many ounces does it weigh?** 48 oz



---



Name ______________________

## Weight

**Essential Question** How can you compare and convert customary units of weight?

Common Core **Measurement and Data—5.MD.A.1**
MATHEMATICAL PRACTICES
**MP1, MP2**

### Unlock the Problem (Real World)

Hector's school is having a model rocket contest. To be in the contest, each rocket must weigh 4 pounds or less. Without any paint, Hector's rocket weighs 62 ounces. If Hector wants to paint his rocket, what is the weight of the most paint he can use?

The **weight** of an object is how heavy the object is.

- What weight does Hector need to convert? 4 pounds to ounces
- After Hector converts the weight, what does he need to do next? He needs to subtract.

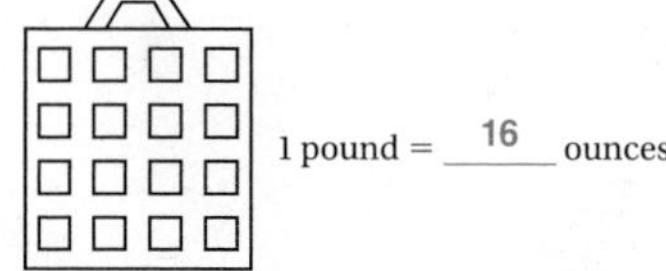


**Use a bar model to write an equation.**

**STEP 1** Convert 4 pounds to ounces.

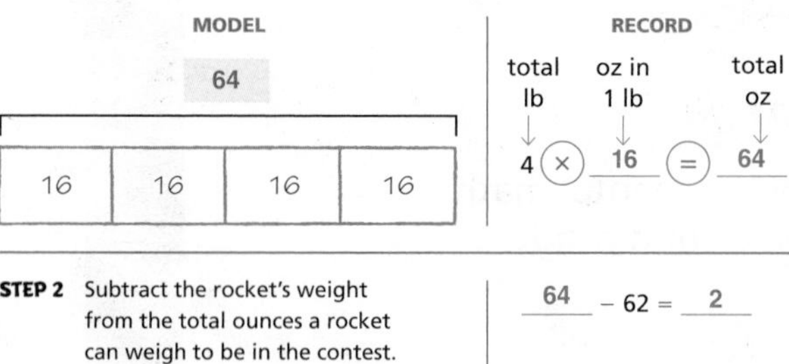


**STEP 2** Subtract the rocket's weight from the total ounces a rocket can weigh to be in the contest.

64 − 62 = 2

So, the weight of the paint can be at most 2 ounces for Hector's model rocket to be in the contest.

Math Talk MATHEMATICAL PRACTICES 1 Make Sense of Problems How did you choose which operation to use to change from pounds to ounces? Explain.

Possible explanation: Since ounces are smaller than pounds, I knew I needed more ounces to make the same weight. So, I needed to multiply by 16, not divide.





---

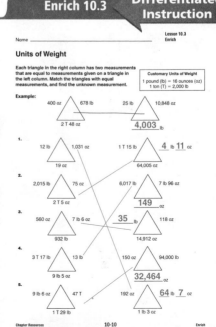

## Reteach 10.3 RtI

Name ______________________ Lesson 10.3 Reteach

### Weight

You can convert one customary unit of weight to another by multiplying or dividing.

Multiply to change from larger to smaller units.

Divide to change from smaller to larger units.

**Customary Units of Weight**
1 pound (lb) = 16 ounces (oz)
1 ton (T) = 2,000 pounds

**Convert 96 ounces to pounds.**

| Step 1 | Step 2 | Step 3 |
|---|---|---|
| Decide: Multiply or (Divide) ounces → pounds smaller → larger | Think: 16 oz = 1 lb so 96 oz = (96 ÷ 16) lb. | Divide. 96 ÷ 16 = 6 |

So, 96 ounces = 6 pounds.

**Convert 4 pounds to ounces.**

| Step 1 | Step 2 | Step 3 |
|---|---|---|
| Decide: (Multiply) or Divide pounds → ounces larger → smaller | Think: 1 lb = 16 oz, so 4 lb = (4 × 16) oz. | Multiply. 4 × 16 = 64 |

So, 4 pounds = 64 ounces.

**Convert.**

1. 14 lb = 224 oz
2. 12,000 lb = 6 T
3. 2 T = 4,000 lb
4. 7 lb = 112 oz
5. 22 lb = 352 oz
6. 16 oz = 1 lb

**Compare. Write <, >, or =.**

7. 1 T < 3,000 lb
8. 3 lb > 43 oz
9. 5 T = 10,000 lb
10. 3 T = 6,000 lb
11. 6 lb = 96 oz
12. 16 T > 6,400 lb

Chapter Resources 10-9 Reteach


---

## Enrich 10.3 Differentiated Instruction

Name ______________________ Lesson 10.3 Enrich

### Units of Weight

**Each triangle in the right column has two measurements that are equal to measurements given on a triangle in the left column. Match the triangles with equal measurements, and find the unknown measurement.**

**Customary Units of Weight**
1 pound (lb) = 16 ounces (oz)
1 ton (T) = 2,000 lb

**Example:** 400 oz, 678 lb, 2 T 48 oz — 25 lb, 10,848 oz, 4,003 lb

1. 12 lb, 1,031 oz, 19 oz — 1 T 15 lb, 4 lb 11 oz, 64,005 oz
2. 2,015 lb, 75 oz, 2 T 5 oz — 6,017 lb, 7 lb 96 oz, 149 oz
3. 560 oz, 7 lb 6 oz, 932 lb — 35 lb, 118 oz, 14,912 oz
4. 3 T 17 lb, 13 lb, 9 lb 5 oz — 150 oz, 94,000 lb, 32,464 oz
5. 9 lb 6 oz, 47 T, 1 T 29 lb — 192 oz, 64 lb 7 oz, 1 lb 3 oz

Chapter Resources 10-10 Enrich

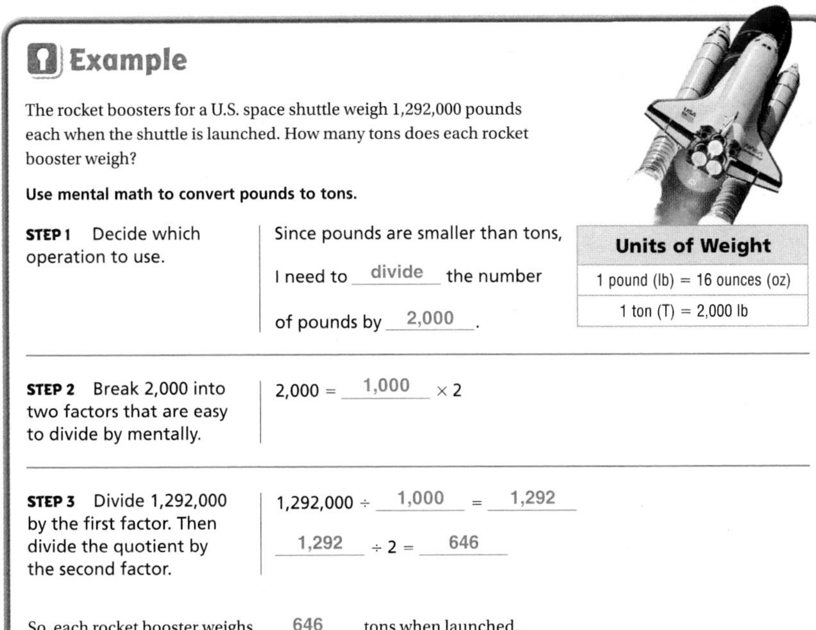

## Example

The rocket boosters for a U.S. space shuttle weigh 1,292,000 pounds each when the shuttle is launched. How many tons does each rocket booster weigh?

**Use mental math to convert pounds to tons.**

| Units of Weight |
|---|
| 1 pound (lb) = 16 ounces (oz) |
| 1 ton (T) = 2,000 lb |

| | |
|---|---|
| **STEP 1** Decide which operation to use. | Since pounds are smaller than tons, I need to divide the number of pounds by 2,000. |
| **STEP 2** Break 2,000 into two factors that are easy to divide by mentally. | 2,000 = 1,000 × 2 |
| **STEP 3** Divide 1,292,000 by the first factor. Then divide the quotient by the second factor. | 1,292,000 ÷ 1,000 = 1,292<br>1,292 ÷ 2 = 646 |

So, each rocket booster weighs 646 tons when launched.

## Share and Show

1. Use the picture to complete each equation.
   - a. 1 pound = 16 ounces
   - b. 2 pounds = 32 ounces
   - c. 3 pounds = 48 ounces
   - d. 4 pounds = 64 ounces
   - e. 5 pounds = 80 ounces

**Convert.**

2. 15 lb = 240 oz
3. 3 T = 6,000 lb
4. 320 oz = 20 lb

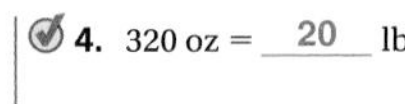

**Math Talk** MATHEMATICAL PRACTICES 2 Reason Quantitatively How can you compare 11 pounds to 175 ounces mentally?

Possible answer: I can convert 10 lb to oz by multiplying by 16 to get 160 oz. Then I can add 16 more oz to find there are 176 oz in 11 lb. So, 11 lb is greater than 175 oz.





## Advanced Learners

Spatial
Individual / Small Group

**Materials** index cards

- Have students write two equivalent weights on two index cards. For example, 48 oz and 3 lb might be two cards. Each student should make five pairs of these cards.
- Students should place the cards facedown in an array.
- Have students take turns picking two cards. If the cards show equivalent weights, the student keeps the cards. Otherwise, the student returns the cards facedown to the array.
- Students may play individually or in groups. If playing individually, they should try to find all the pairs within seven picks. If playing in a group, the student with the most pairs wins.

| 48 oz |
|---|
| 3 lb |

## Example

Introduce this problem by encouraging students who have seen a space shuttle launch in person to share their experiences with the class.

- **Why is division used to solve the problem?** Possible answer: To solve the problem, we must change a smaller unit (pounds) to a larger unit (tons), and the number of units will decrease. Division is used to convert from a smaller unit to a larger unit.

# 3 EXPLAIN

## Share and Show

The first problem connects to the learning model. Have students use the MathBoard to explain their thinking.

Use the checked exercises for Quick Check. Students should show their answers for the Quick Check on the MathBoard.

### Quick Check RtI

**If** a student misses the checked exercises

**Then** Differentiate Instruction with
- Reteach 10.3
- Personal Math Trainer 5.MD.A.1
- RtI Tier 1 Activity (online)

**Math Talk** Use **Math Talk** to focus on students' understanding of using mental math to compare weights.

- **How could you use mental math to check your work when you convert measurements?** Possible answer: I could break the original measurement into parts that are easier to multiply or divide. Then I could perform the operation in my head and compare it to my calculation.

## On Your Own

To help complete the exercises, remind students to refer to the equivalent customary relationships shown in the table on page 598. Encourage students to check their answers.

You may want to give students additional experience in converting units of weight using the activity found in *i*Tools: Measurement • Equivalent Measures • Weight/Mass. *i*Tools can be found at *www.thinkcentral.com.*

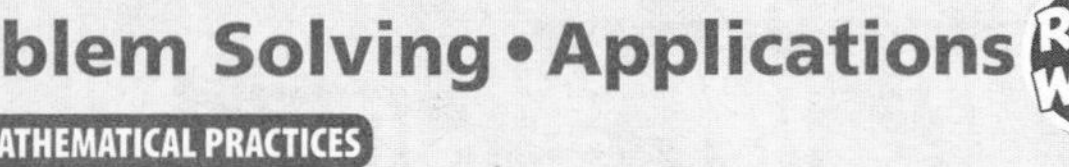


MATHEMATICAL PRACTICES

**MP2 Reason abstractly and quantitatively.** For Exercise 19, make sure students think carefully about which operation to choose. Ask students to consider whether they expect the number of resulting units to be greater than or less than the number of starting units.

Exercise 20 is a multistep problem that requires students to add measurements, convert units, divide, and interpret the remainder.

### Math on the Spot Video Tutor

Use this video to help students model and solve this type of *Think Smarter* problem.

**Math on the Spot** videos are in the Interactive Student Edition and at *www.thinkcentral.com.*

## COMMON ERRORS

**Error** Students use multiplication to change a smaller unit to a larger unit.

**Example**

2 ounces = 32 pounds

**Springboard to Learning** Write the relationships 16 ounces = 1 pound and 2,000 pounds = 1 ton on the board.

Have students identify the smaller unit in each relationship, and compare the number of smaller units to the number of larger units. Then ask students to identify which operation—multiplication or division—is used to change many smaller units into fewer larger units.



---

Name ________________

## On Your Own

**Practice: Copy and Solve** Convert.

5. 23 lb = ■ oz 368
6. 6 T = ■ lb 12,000
7. 144 oz = ■ lb 9
8. 15 T = ■ lb 30,000
9. 352 oz = ■ lb 22
10. 18 lb = ■ oz 288

**Compare. Write <, >, or =.**

11. 130 oz (>) 8 lb
12. 34 lb (=) 544 oz
13. 14 lb (<) 229 oz
14. 16 T (=) 32,000 lb
15. 5 lb (>) 79 oz
16. 85,000 lb (>) 40 T

17. GO DEEPER Bill has a bike that weighs 56 pounds. Magda has a bike that weighs 52 pounds. She adds a bell and basket to her bike. The bell weighs 12 ounces and the basket weighs 2 pounds 8 ounces. Does Magda's bike with its new bell and basket weigh more than Bill's bike? Explain your reasoning.
Bill's bike weighs more. Possible explanation: Bill's bike weighs 896 oz. Magda's bike weighs 832 oz + 12 oz + 40 oz = 884 oz. 896 oz > 884 oz

## Problem Solving • Applications

18. GO DEEPER Rhada has a 5-pound bag of clay. Her craft project requires 5 ounces of clay for each batch of 6 ornaments. If she uses all of the clay, how many ornaments can Rhada make?
96 ornaments

19. MATHEMATICAL PRACTICE 2 **Represent a Problem** Ellis used 48 ounces of rye flour in a bread recipe. Write an expression you could use to find how many pounds of rye flour Ellis used. Explain how the expression represents the problem.
48 ÷ 16; Possible explanation: There are 48 ounces of rye flour and 16 is the number of ounces in a pound. I divide to convert from a larger unit to a smaller one.

20. THINK SMARTER Kevin uses 36 ounces of dried apples and 18 ounces of dried cranberries to make a fruit snack. He plans to sell the snack in $\frac{1}{2}$-pound containers. How may containers will he fill? Will any fruit snack be left over?
6 containers; Yes, 6 ounces will be left over.

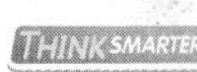 MATHEMATICAL PRACTICES MODEL • REASON • MAKE SENSE

THINKSMARTER **Pose a Problem**

**21.** Kia wants to have 4 pounds of munchies for her party. She has 36 ounces of popcorn and wants the rest to be pretzel sticks. How many ounces of pretzel sticks does she need to buy?

4 pounds = 64 ounces

| 36 ounces | 28 ounces |
|---|---|

So, Kia needs to buy 28 ounces of pretzel sticks.

64 − 36 = 28

Write a new problem using different amounts of snacks. Some weights should be in pounds and others in ounces. Make sure the amount of snacks given is less than the total amount of snacks needed.

**Pose a Problem**

Sample problem and solution are given.

Chita wants to sell 5 pounds of nuts for a fund-raiser. She has sold 42 ounces so far. How many more ounces does she need to sell to meet her goal?

**Draw a bar model for your problem. Then solve.**

5 pounds = 80 ounces

| 42 ounces | 38 ounces |
|---|---|

5 × 16 = 80

She needs to sell 80 ounces of nuts.

80 − 42 = 38

She needs to sell 38 more ounces to meet her goal.

**22.** THINKSMARTER For 22a–22c, select True or False for each statement.

22a. 1,500 lb > 1 T ○ True ● False

22b. 32 oz < 4 lb ● True ○ False

22c. 24 oz < 1 lb 16 oz ● True ○ False





THINKSMARTER

In Problem 21, have students complete the activity by working in pairs or in small groups and then share their work with the class.

THINKSMARTER

Item 22 assesses a student's ability to convert between customary units of weight, ounces, pounds and tons. A student who has answered 22a incorrectly may be comparing the numbers without considering the units. Students who answered 22a and 22b correctly, but answered 22c incorrectly, may not understand a measurement given with two different units, such as 1 lb 16 oz.

## 5 EVALUATE Formative Assessment

### Essential Question

**Using the Language Objective**

**Reflect** Have students draw and label a process in their Math Journal to answer the essential question.

**How can you compare and convert customary units of weight?** Possible answer: First, I use division to convert the smaller unit to the larger unit, or I use multiplication to convert the larger unit to the smaller unit. Then, I use a <, >, or = symbol to compare.

### Math Journal WRITE Math

**Give two examples of items that weigh less than 1 ounce and two examples of items that weigh more than 1 ton.**

## DIFFERENTIATED INSTRUCTION INDEPENDENT ACTIVITIES

**Differentiated Centers Kit**

***Literature***

***A Math Mix-Up***

Students read about a mix-up in customary and metric measurements that led to the NASA's Mars Climate Orbiter crashing into Mars.

***Games***

***2 Steps Forward, 1 Step Back***

Students convert customary and metric units to move along the game path.

## Practice and Homework

Use the Practice and Homework pages to provide students with more practice of the concepts and skills presented in this lesson. Students master their understanding as they complete practice items and then challenge their critical thinking skills with Problem Solving. Use the Write Math section to determine student's understanding of content for this lesson. Encourage students to use their Math Journals to record their answers.

Name ______

**Weight**

COMMON CORE STANDARD—5.MD.A.1
*Convert like measurement units within a given measurement system.*

**Convert.**

1. 96 oz = 6 lb
   total oz ÷ oz in 1 lb = total lb
   96 ÷ 16 = 6
2. 6 T = 12,000 lb
3. 18 lb = 288 oz
4. 3,200 oz = 200 lb
5. 12 T = 24,000 lb
6. 9 lb = 144 oz
7. 7 lb = 112 oz
8. 100 lb = 1,600 oz
9. 60,000 lb = 30 T

**Compare. Write <, >, or =.**

10. 40 oz < 4 lb
11. 80 oz = 5 lb
12. 5,000 lb < 5 T
13. 18,000 lb = 9 T
14. 25 lb > 350 oz
15. 27 oz < 2 lb

16. Mr. Fields ordered 3 tons of gravel for a driveway at a factory. How many pounds of gravel did he order?

    6,000 pounds

17. Sara can take no more than 22 pounds of luggage on a trip. Her suitcase weighs 112 ounces. How many more pounds can she pack without going over the limit?

    15 pounds

18. WRITE Math Give two examples of items that weigh less than 1 ounce and two examples of items that weigh more than 1 ton.

    Check students' examples.





## Common Core PROFESSIONAL DEVELOPMENT Math Talk in Action

*Discuss different ways to solve Exercise 2.*

**Teacher:** When we convert tons to pounds, are we converting a larger unit to a smaller unit, or a smaller unit to a larger unit? Explain your answer.

**Xiao-Chen:** We are converting a larger unit to a smaller unit because a ton represents 2,000 of a smaller unit called pounds.

**Teacher:** Yes. What operation would we use to change a larger unit to a smaller unit? Explain.

**Sam:** I would use multiplication because we will be changing a few larger units to many smaller units.

**Rochelle:** Since 1 ton = 2,000 pounds, we multiply the number of tons by 2,000 to find the number of pounds.

**Teacher:** Correct. Suggest some other ways to solve the problem.

**Bree:** I would use addition and add 2,000 six times.

**Teacher:** How about using a bar model to write an equation?

**Takeko:** I would draw a bar model with 6 equal boxes to show 6 tons.

**Gabe:** And then write 2,000 in each box, because each ton equals 2,000 pounds.

**Christopher:** Then you find 6 groups of 2,000, or $6 \times 2,000 = 12,000$.

## Lesson Check (5.MD.A.1)

1. Paolo's puppy weighed 11 pounds at the vet's office. What is this weight in ounces?

   176 ounces

2. The weight limit on a bridge is 5 tons. What is this weight in pounds?

   10,000 pounds

## Spiral Review (5.NF.A.2, 5.NF.B.7c, 5.MD.A.1)

3. There are 20 guests at a party. The host has 8 gallons of punch. He estimates that each guest will drink 2 cups of punch. If his estimate is correct, how much punch will be left over at the end of the party?

   88 cups

4. A typical lap around a track in the United States has a length of 440 yards. How many laps would need to be completed to run a mile?

   4 laps

5. A recipe for sweet potato casserole calls for $\frac{3}{4}$ cup of milk. Martina has 6 cups of milk. How many sweet potato casseroles can she make with that amount of milk?

   8 casseroles

6. What is the best estimate for the total weight of these cold meats: $1\frac{7}{8}$ pounds of bologna, $1\frac{1}{2}$ pounds of ham, and $\frac{7}{8}$ pound of roast beef?

   $4\frac{1}{2}$ pounds



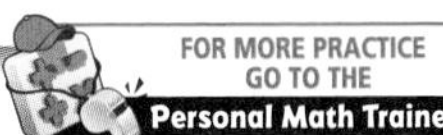




Continue concepts and skills practice with Lesson Check. Use Spiral Review to engage students in previously taught concepts and to promote content retention. Common Core standards are correlated to each section.

LESSON 10.4

# Multistep Measurement Problems

FOCUS COHERENCE RIGOR

## LESSON AT A GLANCE

### F C R Focus:

**Common Core State Standards**

**5.MD.A.1** Convert among different-sized standard measurement units within a given measurement system (e.g., convert 5 cm to 0.05 m), and use these conversions in solving multi-step, real world problems.

**MATHEMATICAL PRACTICES**

**MP1** Make sense of problems and persevere in solving them. **MP2** Reason abstractly and quantitatively. **MP6** Attend to precision.

### F C R Coherence:

**Standards Across the Grades**

| Before | Grade 5 | After |
|---|---|---|
| 4.MD.A.1 | 5.MD.A.1 | 6.RP.A.3d |

### F C R Rigor:

**Level 1: Understand Concepts**....................*Share and Show* (✓ Checked Items)
**Level 2: Procedural Skills and Fluency**.......*On Your Own*
**Level 3: Applications**.................................*Think Smarter and Go Deeper*

### Learning Objective

Convert measurement units to solve multistep problems.

### Language Objective

Students brainstorm with a team some possible procedures for solving multistep problems that include measurement conversions.

### Materials

MathBoard

F C R For more about how *GO Math!* fosters **Coherence** within the Content Standards and Mathematical Progressions for this chapter, see page 583J.

## About the Math

**Professional Development**

### MP1 Make sense of problems and persevere in solving them.

Mathematically proficient students start by explaining to themselves the meaning of a problem and looking for entry points to its solution. Faced with a multistep problem like those in this lesson, they will recognize that the application of a single algorithm may provide the beginning of a solution but will, by itself, be insufficient for solving the problem.

Reading the opening problem in the lesson on page 603, for example, the student will note that four units are mentioned, cups, days, weeks, and quarts. The fact that cups and quarts are both measures of capacity will suggest that at some point, it will probably be necessary to convert those measures to a single unit. This observation, in turn, will lead the student to conclude that several steps will be needed to solve the problem, opening a logical path to a solution.

Professional Development Videos

SE Interactive Student Edition

Personal Math Trainer

Math on the Spot

Animated Math Models

*i*Tools: Measurement

HMH Mega Math

## Daily Routines

**Common Core**

### Problem of the Day 10.4

Carmen walked 75 feet from her house to the corner and then 4 blocks to the library. If each block was 150 feet long, what was the total distance that she walked? 675 feet

### Vocabulary

- Interactive Student Edition
- Multimedia eGlossary

### Fluency Builder

**Customary Conversions** Have students work in pairs to practice length, capacity, and weight equivalents.

Each pair should prepare 12 index cards labeled with the units shown below. Students shuffle the cards and place them in a pile facedown. Students take turns drawing a card and stating a fact involving the unit shown on the card. For example, if a student draws a card labeled "foot," the student might say "12 inches equal 1 foot" or "3 feet equal 1 yard." The other student checks the answer for accuracy and then draws a new card. If there is time, the cards can be reshuffled and the activity continued. You might choose to impose the rule that after reshuffling, students are required to state a different fact about each unit than was stated the first time around.

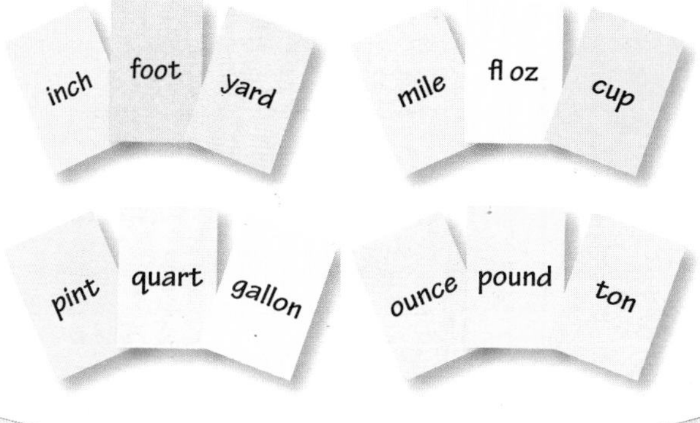


# 1 ENGAGE

## with the Interactive Student Edition

### Essential Question

How can you solve multistep problems that include measurement conversions?

### Making Connections

Invite students to tell you what they know about airplanes.

**Have you ever flown in an airplane? What characteristics of an airplane are different than a pickup truck? Than a helicopter? A boat? What characteristics of an airplane are the same as a pickup truck? A helicopter? A boat?**

### Learning Activity

What is the problem the students are trying to solve? Connect the story to the problem.

- **How much does the airplane weigh?** 440 tons
- **How much does the pickup truck weigh?** 5,128 pounds
- **Which of the two weighs more?** the airplane
- **What are you being asked to find?** about how many pickup trucks equal the weight of one airplane

### Literacy and Mathematics

Choose one or more of the following activities.

- Write a postcard to a friend about a real or imagined trip you took on an airplane. Describe where you went, what you did, and what it was like on the airplane.
- Write the word *measurement* on the board. Underline the suffix *–ment*. Explain that the suffix forms nouns and indicates the result or product of an action. Elicit words that students know that have the suffix *–ment* (*enjoyment, management, refreshment*). Then have students discuss the meanings of the words with a partner.

# 2 EXPLORE

**Common Core** 5.MD.A.1 Convert among different-sized standard measurement units within a given measurement system (e.g., convert 5 cm to 0.05 m), and use these conversions in solving multi-step, real world problems.

## Unlock the Problem

**Common Core MATHEMATICAL PRACTICES**

**You know how to convert cups to pints, quarts, and gallons. Read the problem to discover a situation where you have to carry out conversions involving cups and weeks.**

**MP1 Make sense of problems and persevere in solving them.**

Guide students to see that they must make *two* conversions to solve the problem. Ask:

- **The problem states that 2 cups of water drip each day but it asks for the amount that drips in 2 weeks. How can you convert the amount from days to weeks?** Multiply 2 cups per day by the number of days in 2 weeks, 14.
- **Once you know the number of cups of water that dripped in 2 weeks, have you solved the problem? Explain.** No; you must convert the number of cups to the number of quarts.

After students solve the problem, ask:

- **Describe another way you could have solved the problem.** Possible answer: I could have converted the amount of water dripped each day to quarts, and then converted the number of quarts dripped each day to the number of quarts dripped in 14 days.

**MP6 Attend to precision.**

- **How is converting units of time similar to converting customary units of capacity?** Each time unit is made up of a certain number of smaller time units. For example, 1 week = 7 days and 1 day = 24 hours. You can convert between them just as you do with measurements of capacity.

## ELL Strategy:
### Understand Context

Write these word pairs on the board and read them aloud with students:

weigh way weight wait

- **What do you notice about each word pair?** They sound the same but are spelled differently and have different meanings.
- **Listen as I read a sentence. Point to the word on the board that completes it:**
  **How much does the book** weigh**?**
  **Which** way **should we go?**
  **Please** wait **for me after school.**
  **What is the** weight **of one egg?**



---

Lesson 10.4

Name ____________

## Multistep Measurement Problems

**Essential Question** How can you solve multistep problems that include measurement conversions?

**Common Core** Measurement and Data—5.MD.A.1
MATHEMATICAL PRACTICES
MP1, MP2, MP6

### Unlock the Problem

A leaky faucet in Jarod's house drips 2 cups of water each day. After 2 weeks of dripping, the faucet is fixed. If it dripped the same amount each day, how many quarts of water dripped from Jarod's leaky faucet in 2 weeks?

**Use the steps to solve the multistep problem.**

**STEP 1**

Record the information you are given.

The faucet drips __2__ cups of water each day.

The faucet drips for __2__ weeks.

**STEP 2**

Find the total amount of water dripped in 2 weeks.

Since you are given the amount of water dripped each day, you must convert 2 weeks into days and multiply.

Think: There are 7 days in 1 week.

| cups each day | | days in 2 weeks | | total cups |
|---|---|---|---|---|
| 2 | × | 14 | = | 28 |

The faucet drips __28__ cups in 2 weeks.

**STEP 3**

Convert from cups to quarts.

Think: There are 2 cups in 1 pint.

There are 2 pints in 1 quart.

__28__ cups = __14__ pints

__14__ pints = __7__ quarts

So, Jarod's leaky faucet drips __7__ quarts of water in 2 weeks.

- What if the faucet dripped for 4 weeks before it was fixed? How many quarts of water would have leaked? __14 quarts__





---

## Reteach 10.4

Name ____________ Lesson 10.4 Reteach

### Multistep Measurement Problems

**An ice cream parlor donated 6 containers of ice cream to a local elementary school. Each container holds 3 gallons of ice cream. If each student is served 1 cup of ice cream, how many students can be served?**

**Step 1** Record the information you are given.

There are __6__ containers of ice cream.

Each container holds __3__ gallons of ice cream.

**Step 2** Find the total amount of ice cream in the 6 containers.

6 × 3 gallons = __18__ gallons of ice cream

**Step 3** Convert from gallons to cups.

There are __4__ quarts in 1 gallon, so 18 gallons = __72__ quarts.

There are __2__ pints in 1 quart, so 72 quarts = __144__ pints.

There are __2__ cups in 1 pint, so 144 pints = __288__ cups.

So, __288__ students can be served 1 cup of ice cream.

**Solve.**

1. A cargo truck weighs 8,750 pounds. The weight limit for a certain bridge is 5 tons. How many pounds of cargo can be added to the truck before it exceeds the weight limit for the bridge? __1,250 pounds__
2. A plumber uses 16 inches of tubing to connect each washing machine in a laundry to the water source. He wants to install 18 washing machines. How many yards of tubing will he need? __8 yards__
3. Larry has 9 gallons of paint. He uses 10 quarts to paint his kitchen and 3 gallons to paint his living room. How many pints of paint will be left? __28 pints__
4. Ketisha is practicing for a marathon by running around a track that is 440 yards long. Yesterday she ran around the track 20 times. How many miles did she run? __5 miles__

Chapter Resources 10-11 Reteach


---

## Enrich 10.4

**Differentiated Instruction**

Name ____________ Lesson 10.4 Enrich

### Adding and Subtracting Measures

**Write each sum or difference in two ways. The first answer is given.** Possible answers are given.

1. 3 ft 9 in. + 7 ft 5 in. __11 ft 2 in.; 134 in.__
2. $2\frac{1}{2}$ yd − $1\frac{3}{4}$ ft __69 in.; $5\frac{3}{4}$ ft__
3. 9 mi 3,500 ft + 8 mi 1,990 ft __18 mi 210 ft; 18 mi 70 yd__
4. 9 yd 1 ft 11 in. − 4 yd 2 ft 8 in. __4 yd 2 ft 3 in.; 14 ft 3 in.__
5. 8 lb 12 oz + 3 lb 6 oz __12 lb 2 oz; 194 oz__
6. 6 T 400 lb − 4 T 1,000 lb __1 T 1,400 lb; 3,400 lb__
7. 12 gal 3 qt + 5 gal 2 qt __18 gal 1 qt; 73 qt__
8. 8 pt 3 fl oz − 2 pt 9 fl oz __5 pt 10 fl oz; 90 fl oz__
9. Write Math **Explain** how you found the difference in Exercise 4.
   Possible explanation: I converted both lengths to inches. So, 9 yd 1 ft 11 in. = 347 in., and 4 yd 2 ft 8 in. = 176 in. Then I subtracted 347 in. − 176 in. = 171 in. To convert to feet, I divided 171 by 12, which gave me 14 ft 3 in. To convert to yards, I divided 14 by 3, which gave me 4 yd 2 ft. I added the 3 in. to get 4 yd 2 ft 3 in.

Chapter Resources 10-12 Enrich

## Example

A carton of large, Grade A eggs weighs about 1.5 pounds. If a carton holds a dozen eggs, how many ounces does each egg weigh?

**STEP 1**

In ounces, find the weight of a carton of eggs.

Think: 1 pound = 16 ounces

Weight of a carton (in ounces):

| total lb | | oz in 1 lb | | total oz |
|---|---|---|---|---|
| ↓ | | ↓ | | ↓ |
| 1.5 | × | 16 | = | 24 |

The carton of eggs weighs about 24 ounces.

**STEP 2**

In ounces, find the weight of each egg in a carton.

Think: 1 carton (dozen eggs) = 12 eggs

Weight of each egg (in ounces):

| total oz | | eggs in 1 carton | | oz of 1 egg |
|---|---|---|---|---|
| ↓ | | ↓ | | ↓ |
| 24 | ÷ | 12 | = | 2 |

So, each egg weighs about 2 ounces.

### Share and Show

Solve.

1. After each soccer practice, Scott runs 4 sprints of 20 yards each. If he continues his routine, how many practices will it take for Scott to have sprinted a total of 2 miles combined?

   Scott sprints 80 yards each practice.

   Since there are 3,520 yards in 2 miles, he will need to continue his routine for

   44 practices.

2. A worker at a mill is loading 5-lb bags of flour into boxes to deliver to a local warehouse. Each box holds 12 bags of flour. If the warehouse orders 3 Tons of flour, how many boxes are needed to fulfill the order?

   100 boxes

3. Cory brings five 1-gallon jugs of juice to serve during parent night at his school. If the paper cups he is using for drinks can hold 8 fluid ounces, how many drinks can Cory serve for parent night?

   80 drinks

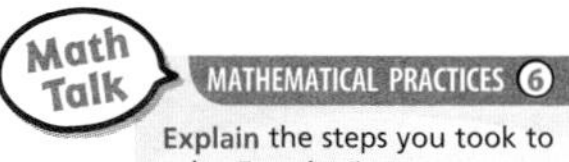

Math Talk
MATHEMATICAL PRACTICES 6
Explain the steps you took to solve Exercise 2.


Possible explanation: First, I found the pounds of flour in each box. Then I converted 3 Tons to pounds and divided the pounds of flour ordered by the pounds in each box.





## Advanced Learners

Verbal / spatial
Individual

**Materials** road maps

- Maps for this activity should provide a way for students to determine distances between major cities–either distance tables or mileages written directly beside the highways. Motivated students might be encouraged to use the map scale and a ruler to calculate distances.
- Have each student choose a city on a road map as a starting point for a trip. Students should map out a circular round-trip that will include at least three other cities before returning to the starting point.
- Ask students to estimate the total length of the trip before they make any calculations.
- Students should calculate the total length of the journey in miles, yards, feet, and inches.

## Example

**Describe how you could have solved the problem by first finding the weight of each egg in pounds.** I could have divided the weight in pounds of a carton by 12 to find the weight of each egg in pounds. Then I could have multiplied the quotient by the number of ounces in 1 pound.

**Which method of solving the problem is easier? Why?** Possible answer: Converting pounds to ounces is easier because it involves only whole numbers.

### Share and Show

The first problem connects to the learning model. Have students use the MathBoard to explain their thinking.

Use the checked exercises for **Quick Check**. Students should show their answers for the Quick Check on the Math Board.

**If** a student misses the checked exercises

**Then** **Differentiate Instruction** with

- Reteach 10.4
- Personal Math Trainer 5.MD.A.1
- RtI Tier 1 Activity (online)

**Math Talk** Use **Math Talk** to emphasize the importance of first organizing the information when solving a multistep problem.

- **Could you have followed a different sequence of steps? Explain.** Possible answer: yes; I could have found the number of 5-lb bags equal to 3 tons and then divided that by the number of bags that would fit in each box.

## On Your Own

**MP4 Model with mathematics.** For Problem 5, students may calculate the length of the string in inches and then divide by 4 to find the incorrect answer, 84 lights. Encourage them to draw a sketch to see that, because no lights appear on the first 16 inches of the string, the correct answer is 3 less than 84, or 81.

**GO DEEPER**

Problem 7 requires students to think carefully about operations with fractions. After converting tons to pounds, students must find $\frac{1}{40}$ of the elephant's weight in order to solve. They can do this by multiplying the weight in pounds of the elephant by $\frac{1}{40}$ or dividing the weight by 40.

**THINK SMARTER**

Problem 9 requires students to generalize the method they have used to solve most of the exercises. In other problems, they have worked from smaller rates like 2 cups per day to larger ones like 14 quarts per 2 weeks. Here they must reverse the process, working from the larger rate of 6 pounds per gallon to a smaller one, 24 ounces per quart. Students might also use proportional reasoning: since 1 gallon weighs 6 pounds, $\frac{1}{4}$ gallon (1 quart) must weigh $\frac{1}{4} \times 6$, or $1\frac{1}{2}$ pounds, which they can convert to 24 ounces.

### COMMON ERRORS

**Error** Students make the first conversion in a multistep measurement problem but fail to make the second conversion.

**Example** 12 ft per min = ? yd per hr

Solution: 4 yd per hr

**Springboard to Learning** Before students begin solving a problem, have them write the units involved in the problem. Then outline or diagram the conversions they will make to solve the problem, in the order they will make them. In the example, they might use arrows to write ft per min → yd per min and then yd per min → yd per hr.



Name ________________________________

## On Your Own

**Solve.**

4. GO DEEPER A science teacher collects 18 pints of lake water for a lab she is teaching. The lab requires each student to use 4 fluid ounces of lake water. If 68 students are participating, how many pints of lake water will the teacher have left over?

1 pint

5. MATHEMATICAL PRACTICE 4 **Use Diagrams** A string of decorative lights is 28 feet long. The first light on the string is 16 inches from the plug. If the lights on the string are spaced 4 inches apart, how many lights are there on the string? Draw a picture to help you solve the problem.

81 lights

6. When Elena's car moves forward such that each tire makes one full rotation, the car has traveled 72 inches. How many full rotations will the tires need to make for Elena's car to travel 10 yards?

5 full rotations

7. GO DEEPER A male African elephant weighs 7 tons. If a male African lion at the local zoo weighs $\frac{1}{40}$ of the weight of the male African elephant, how many pounds does the lion weigh?

350 pounds

8. Darnell rented a moving truck. The weight of the empty truck was 7,860 pounds. When Darnell filled the truck with his items, it weighed 6 tons. What was the weight in pounds of the items that Darnell placed in the truck?

4,140 pounds

9. THINK SMARTER A gallon of unleaded gasoline weighs about 6 pounds. About how many ounces does 1 quart of unleaded gasoline weigh? HINT: 1 quart = $\frac{1}{4}$ of a gallon

about 24 ounces

 MATHEMATICAL PRACTICES COMMUNICATE • PERSEVERE • CONSTRUCT ARGUMENTS

## Unlock the Problem (Real World)

10. THINKSMARTER At a local animal shelter there are 12 small-size dogs and 5 medium-size dogs. Every day, the small-size dogs are each given 12.5 ounces of dry food and the medium-size dogs are each given 18 ounces of the same dry food. How many pounds of dry food does the shelter serve in one day?

a. What are you asked to find? the total weight, in pounds, of the dry food served in one day

b. What information will you use? There are 12 small-size dogs that eat 12.5 ounces of dry food each. There are 5 medium-size dogs that eat 18 ounces of dry food each.

c. What conversion will you need to do to solve the problem? The amount of food eaten each day is given in ounces, and I need to know pounds. So, I will convert from ounces to pounds.

d. Show the steps you use to solve the problem.

small-size dogs:
$12 \times 12.5$ ounces $= 150$ ounces

medium-size dogs:
$5 \times 18$ ounces $= 90$ ounces

total food served (in ounces):
$150 + 90 = 240$ ounces

Conversion: $240 \div 16 = 15$ pounds

e. Complete the sentences. The small-size dogs eat a total of 150 ounces of dry food each day.

The medium-size dogs eat a total of 90 ounces of dry food each day.

The shelter serves 240 ounces, or 15 pounds, of dry food each day.



Personal Math Trainer

11. THINKSMARTER+ Gus is painting his house. He uses 2 quarts of paint per hour. Gus paints for 8 hours. How many gallons of paint did he use? Show your work.

4 gallons; Possible solution: 2 quarts $\times$ 8 hours $=$ 16 quarts; 1 gallon $=$ 4 quarts; 16 quarts $\div$ 4 quarts $=$ 4 gallons



## DIFFERENTIATED INSTRUCTION | INDEPENDENT ACTIVITIES

**Differentiated Centers Kit**

*Literature*
***A Math Mix-Up***

Students read about a mix-up in customary and metric measurements that led to the NASA's Mars Climate Orbiter crashing into Mars.

*Games*
***2 Steps Forward, 1 Step Back***

Students convert customary and metric units to move along the game path.

# 4 ELABORATE

## Unlock the Problem

MATHEMATICAL PRACTICES

THINKSMARTER

Problem 10 requires students to add an additional step to the sequence of steps they have been using in this lesson.

### Math on the Spot Video Tutor

Use this video to help students model and solve this type of *Think Smarter* problem.

**Math on the Spot** videos are in the Interactive Student Edition and at *www.thinkcentral.com*.

**Personal Math Trainer**

Be sure to assign this problem to students in the Personal Math Trainer. It features a video to help them model and answer the problem. The problem requires students to understand a real-world problem and to convert customary measures of capacity. Students who find the incorrect number of gallons may not know the equivalent measures of capacity or may have misunderstood what was needed in the word problem. Students who find the correct answer but cannot explain their reasoning may need help using math vocabulary.

# 5 EVALUATE Formative Assessment

## Essential Question

### Using the Language Objective

**Reflect** Have students brainstorm with a team some possible procedures to answer the essential question.

**How can you solve multistep problems that include measurement conversions?** Possible answer: First, record the information you are given. Next, convert one of the units you are given to one of the units you are looking for. Finally, convert the second unit you are given to the second unit you are looking for.

## Math Journal WRITE Math

**An object moves on a conveyor belt at a speed of 60 inches per second. Explain how you could convert the speed to feet per minute.**

## Practice and Homework

Use the Practice and Homework pages to provide students with more practice of the concepts and skills presented in this lesson. Students master their understanding as they complete practice items and then challenge their critical thinking skills with Problem Solving. Use the Write Math section to determine student's understanding of content for this lesson. Encourage students to use their Math Journals to record their answers.

Name ______________________

**Practice and Homework Lesson 10.4**

### Multistep Measurement Problems

COMMON CORE STANDARD—5.MD.A.1 *Convert like measurement units within a given measurement system.*

**Solve.**

1. A cable company has 5 miles of cable to install. How many 100-yard lengths of cable can be cut?

   Think: 1,760 yards = 1 mile. So the cable company has 5 × 1,760, or 8,800 yards of cable.

   Divide. 8,800 ÷ 100 = 88

   88 lengths

2. Afton made a chicken dish for dinner. She added a 10-ounce package of vegetables and a 14-ounce package of rice to 40 ounces of chicken. What was the total weight of the chicken dish in pounds?

   4 pounds

3. A jar contains 26 fluid ounces of spaghetti sauce. How many cups of spaghetti sauce do 4 jars contain?

   13 cups

4. Coach Kent brings 3 quarts of sports drink to soccer practice. He gives the same amount of the drink to each of his 16 players. How many ounces of the drink does each player get?

   6 ounces

5. Leslie needs 324 inches of fringe to put around the edge of a tablecloth. The fringe comes in lengths of 10 yards. If Leslie buys 1 package of fringe, how many feet of fringe will she have left over?

   3 feet

6. An office supply company is shipping a case of wooden pencils to a store. There are 64 boxes of pencils in the case. If each box of pencils weighs 2.5 ounces, what is the weight, in pounds, of the case of wooden pencils?

   10 pounds

### Problem Solving (Real World)

7. A pitcher contains 40 fluid ounces of iced tea. Shelby pours 3 cups of iced tea. How many pints of iced tea are left in the pitcher?

   1 pint

8. Olivia ties 2.5 feet of ribbon onto one balloon. How many yards of ribbon does Olivia need for 18 balloons?

   15 yards

9. **WRITE** Math An object moves on a conveyor belt at a speed of 60 inches per second. Explain how you could convert the speed to feet per minute.

   Check students' explanations.





## Common Core PROFESSIONAL DEVELOPMENT Math Talk in Action

*Discuss different ways to solve Exercise 6.*

**Teacher:** What information are you given in this problem? And what do you want to find out?

**Amira:** I know that one box of pencils weighs 2.5 ounces. I want to know the weight of 64 boxes in pounds.

**Teacher:** How can you tell that several steps will be needed to solve the problem?

**Franklin:** I will need to convert the weight of 1 box to the weight of 64 boxes. But I will also need to convert ounces to pounds.

**Teacher:** That's right. Can you describe a method you could use to solve the problem?

**Raven:** Since one box weighs 2.5 ounces, 64 boxes must weigh 64 × 2.5 = 160 ounces. I know there are 16 ounces in a pound, so 64 boxes must weigh 160 ÷ 16 = 10 pounds.

**Teacher:** Is there another way to solve the problem?

**Danny:** I used mental math to calculate 4 × 2.5 = 10 and 16 × 2.5 = 40. So, I know that 16 boxes weigh 40 ounces. Since 4 × 16 = 64, 64 boxes will weigh 4 × 40, or 160 ounces. I divided 160 ÷ 16 = 10 mentally to find the weight in pounds. So, 64 boxes weigh 10 pounds.

**Teacher:** Which method do you think is easier?

**Belle:** When the numbers work out, I think it's easier to use mental math.

## Lesson Check (5.MD.A.1)

1. Leah is buying curtains for her bedroom window. She wants the curtains to hang from the top of the window to the floor. The window is 4 feet high. The bottom of the window is $2\frac{1}{2}$ feet above the floor. How many inches long should Leah's curtains be?

   78 inches

2. Brady buys 3 gallons of fertilizer for his lawn. After he finishes spraying the lawn, he has 1 quart of fertilizer left over. How many quarts of fertilizer did Brady spray on the lawn?

   11 quarts

## Spiral Review (5.OA.B.3, 5.MD.A.1, 5.NF.B.7b)

3. A jump rope is 9 feet long. How long is the jump rope in yards?

   3 yards

4. Fill in the blanks to make the following statement true.

   8 cups = 2 quarts = 4 pints.

5. What is the unknown number in Sequence 2 in the chart?

| Sequence Number | 1 | 2 | 3 | 5 | 7 |
|---|---|---|---|---|---|
| Sequence 1 | 3 | 6 | 9 | 15 | 21 |
| Sequence 2 | 6 | 12 | 18 | 30 | ? |

   42

6. A farmer divides 20 acres of land into $\frac{1}{4}$-acre sections. Into how many sections does the farmer divide her land?

   80 sections

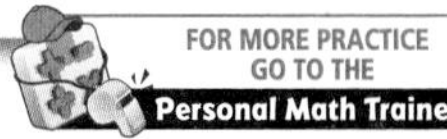






Continue concepts and skills practice with Lesson Check. Use Spiral Review to engage students in previously taught concepts and to promote content retention. Common Core standards are correlated to each section.

# Mid-Chapter Checkpoint

LESSONS 10.1 TO 10.4

## Formative Assessment

Use the **Mid-Chapter Checkpoint** to assess students' learning and progress in the first half of the chapter. The formative assessment provides the opportunity to adjust teaching methods for individual or whole class instruction.

Name ______

## Mid-Chapter Checkpoint

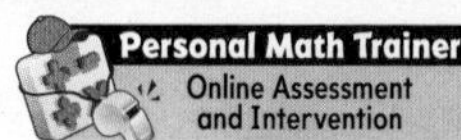

### Vocabulary

**Choose the best term from the box.**

| Vocabulary |
|---|
| capacity |
| length |
| weight |

1. The __weight__ of an object is how heavy the object is. (p. 597)
2. The __capacity__ of a container is the amount the container can hold. (p. 591)

### Concepts and Skills

**Convert.** (5.MD.A.1)

3. 5 mi = __8,800__ yd
4. 48 qt = __12__ gal
5. 9 T = __18,000__ lb
6. 336 oz = __21__ lb
7. 14 ft = __4__ yd __2__ ft
8. 11 pt = __176__ fl oz

**Compare. Write <, >, or =.** (5.MD.A.1)

9. 96 fl oz (<) 13 c
10. 25 lb (>) 384 oz
11. 8 yd (=) 288 in.

**Solve.** (5.MD.A.1)

12. A standard coffee mug has a capacity of 16 fluid ounces. If Annie needs to fill 26 mugs with coffee, how many total quarts of coffee does she need?

__13 quarts__





## Data-Driven Decision Making RtI

Based on the results of the Mid-Chapter Checkpoint, use the following resources to strengthen individual or whole class instruction.

| Item | Lesson | Standard | Common Error | Personal Math Trainer | Intervene With |
|---|---|---|---|---|---|
| 3, 7, 11 | 10.1 | 5.MD.A.1 | May use the wrong operation to compare and convert customary units of length | 5.MD.A.1 | R—10.1 |
| 4, 8–9 | 10.2 | 5.MD.A.1 | May use the wrong operation to compare and convert customary units of capacity | 5.MD.A.1 | R—10.2 |
| 5–6, 10 | 10.3 | 5.MD.A.1 | May use the wrong operation to compare and convert customary units of weight | 5.MD.A.1 | R—10.3 |
| 12 | 10.4 | 5.MD.A.1 | May have performed only one of the two needed unit conversions | 5.MD.A.1 | R—10.4 |

**Key: R**—Reteach (in the *Chapter Resources*)

**13.** The length of a classroom is 34 feet. What is this measurement in yards and feet? (5.MD.A.1)

11 yards 1 foot

**14.** Charlie's puppy, Max, weighs 8 pounds. How many ounces does Max weigh? (5.MD.A.1)

128 ounces

**15.** Milton purchases a 5-gallon aquarium for his bedroom. To fill the aquarium with water, he uses a container with a capacity of 1 quart. How many times will Milton fill and empty the container before the aquarium is full? (5.MD.A.1)

20

**16.** GO DEEPER Sarah uses a recipe to make 2 gallons of her favorite mixed-berry juice. Two of the containers she plans to use to store the juice have a capacity of 1 quart. The rest of the containers have a capacity of 1 pint. How many pint-sized containers will Sarah need? (5.MD.A.1)

12

**17.** The average length of a female white-beaked dolphin is about 111 inches. What is this length in feet and inches? (5.MD.A.1)

9 feet 3 inches







## Data-Driven Decision Making RtI

Based on the results of the Mid-Chapter Checkpoint, use the following resources to strengthen individual or whole class instruction.

| Item | Lesson | Standard | Common Error | Personal Math Trainer | Intervene With |
|---|---|---|---|---|---|
| 13, 17 | 10.1 | 5.MD.A.1 | May use the wrong conversion factor to convert customary units of length | 5.MD.A.1 | R—10.1 |
| 14 | 10.3 | 5.MD.A.1 | May use the wrong conversion factor to convert customary units of weight | 5.MD.A.1 | R—10.3 |
| 15–16 | 10.2 | 5.MD.A.1 | May use the wrong conversion factor to convert customary units of capacity | 5.MD.A.1 | R—10.2 |

**Key: R**—Reteach (in the *Chapter Resources*)

LESSON 10.5

# Metric Measures

FOCUS COHERENCE RIGOR

## LESSON AT A GLANCE

### F C R Focus:

**Common Core State Standards**

**5.MD.A.1** Convert among different-sized standard measurement units within a given measurement system (e.g., convert 5 cm to 0.05 m), and use these conversions in solving multi-step, real world problems.

**MATHEMATICAL PRACTICES**

**MP2** Reason abstractly and quantitatively. **MP6** Attend to precision. **MP8** Look for and express regularity in repeated reasoning.

### F C R Coherence:

**Standards Across the Grades**

| Before | Grade 5 | After |
|---|---|---|
| 4.MD.A.1 | 5.MD.A.1 | 6.RP.A.3d |

### F C R Rigor:

**Level 1:** Understand Concepts....................*Share and Show* (Checked Items)
**Level 2:** Procedural Skills and Fluency.......*On Your Own*
**Level 3:** Applications.................................*Think Smarter and Go Deeper*

### Learning Objective

Compare, contrast, and convert metric units.

### Language Objective

Students use a sports example to show how you can compare and convert metric units.

### Materials

MathBoard

F C R For more about how *GO Math!* fosters **Coherence** within the Content Standards and Mathematical Progressions for this chapter, see page 583J.

## About the Math

**Professional Development**

### Teaching for Depth

The ability to convert metric measures is not only a math skill. In a more general way, it is also a vocational skill for some occupations and a useful skill for those who travel outside of the United States.

It is much simpler to convert between two metric units than to convert between two customary units because metric units are related by powers of 10. To convert between two metric units, simply multiply or divide by a power of 10 such as 10, 100, or 1,000. Usually, these conversions can be performed using only mental math.

Your students may find it interesting if you take the time to demonstrate how to convert distances, such as 24 miles to inches and 24 kilometers to millimeters. One conversion takes minutes, the other seconds.

Professional Development Videos

 Personal Math Trainer

 Math on the Spot

 Animated Math Models

*i*T *i*Tools: Measurement

 HMH Mega Math

# Daily Routines

**Common Core**

## Problem of the Day 10.5

Mr. Reynolds used 2 pounds of oats to make trail mix. How many ounces of oats did he use? 32 ounces

**Vocabulary** **dekameter**

- Interactive Student Edition
- Multimedia eGlossary

## Fluency Builder

**Comparing and Ordering** On separate index cards, have each student write five decimals that are between 1 and 3. At least two numbers should have a digit in the thousandths place.

Collect and redistribute the cards. Then have students order the five decimals using a number line. They should then write the relationships among the five decimals using the symbols $<$, $>$, and $=$.

| 1.25 | 2.571 |
|---|---|
| 1.7 | 2.9 |
| 2.128 | |

# 1 ENGAGE

**with the Interactive Student Edition**

## Essential Question

How can you compare and convert metric units?

## Making Connections

Invite students to tell you what they know about measurement.

**What are some units of measurement that you know?** Answers will vary. **Which units of measurement measure length?** Possible answers: inch, foot, yard, meter, centimeter, kilometer, mile **Which units of measurement measure weight or mass?** Answers will vary. Possible answers: pound, ounce, gram, kilogram, ton

## Learning Activity

What is the problem the students are trying to solve? Connect the story to the problem.

- **How much plant food is in the bucket?** 1.4 liters
- **How much plant food can the eyedropper hold?** 1 milliliter
- **How many flowers does the neighbor feed with 1 eyedropper full of plant food?** 1
- **What are you being asked to find?** how many flowers can be fed with the plant food in the bucket

## Literacy and Mathematics

Choose one or more of the following activities.

- Have students plan and draw a garden that they would like to plant. Have them label it with the different types of plants that they would include in the garden.
- Have students ask each other questions about how they would go about solving the problem. Have them write another scenario involving measurement that could be solved using the same method.

# 2 EXPLORE

**Common Core** **5.MD.A.1** Convert among different-sized standard measurement units within a given measurement system (e.g., convert 5 cm to 0.05 m), and use these conversions in solving multi-step, real world problems.

## Unlock the Problem

**MATHEMATICAL PRACTICES**

**MP6 Attend to precision.**

Discuss the units in the table. Have students note that the units in the center of the table are the base units for length, capacity, and mass. Each unit is one power of 10 greater than the unit to its right and one power of 10 smaller than the unit on its left.

## One Way

**MP8 Look for and express regularity in repeated reasoning.** Refer to the table and point out that because we divide by 10 to change meters to dekameters, divide by 10 to change dekameters to hectometers, and divide by 10 to change hectometers to kilometers, we can simply divide by 1,000 ($10 \times 10 \times 10$) to perform the conversion in one step.

**Math Talk** Use **Math Talk** to focus on students' understanding of using powers of 10 in converting metric measures.

- **Which is greater, 1,000 milligrams or 1 gram? Explain.** They are the same amount. Since milli- is 3 powers of 10 smaller than gram, I can divide the number of milligrams by 1,000 to find the number of grams. 1,000 milligrams = 1 gram.

**GO DEEPER**

Advanced learners may want to know if there are larger and smaller units in the metric system. Explain that scientists do use prefixes such as mega- (million times), giga- (billion times), micro- (millionth part), and nano- (billionth part). Ask if students have seen these prefixes in familiar words. Possible answers: megabyte, gigabyte, microbiology, and nanotechnology

## ELL Strategy: Understand Context

Write *hole* and *whole* on the board and read them aloud with students.

- **What do you notice?** The words sound the same but are spelled differently and have different meanings.
- **As I read each sentence, point to the word on the board that completes it: How deep is that __hole__? 7 is a __whole__ number.**
- Point out that *unit* can mean "number." It can also mean "part of something," such as a unit about measurement in math class.

---

Name ______________________

Lesson 10.5

## Metric Measures

**Essential Question** How can you compare and convert metric units?

**Common Core** Measurement and Data—5.MD.A.1
MATHEMATICAL PRACTICES MP2, MP6, MP8

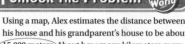

### Unlock the Problem (Real World)

Using a map, Alex estimates the distance between his house and his grandparent's house to be about 15,000 meters. About how many kilometers away from his grandparent's house does Alex live?

- Underline the sentence that tells you what you are trying to find.
- Circle the measurement you need to convert.

The metric system is based on place value. Each unit is related to the next largest or next smallest unit by a power of 10.

**One Way** Convert 15,000 meters to kilometers.

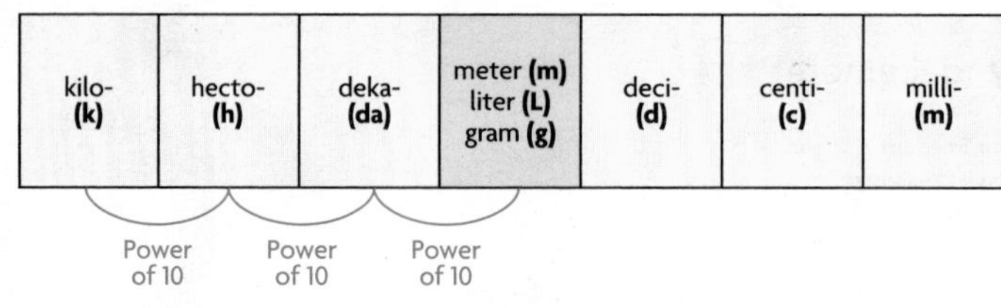

| kilo- (k) | hecto- (h) | deka- (da) | meter (m) liter (L) gram (g) | deci- (d) | centi- (c) | milli- (m) |
|---|---|---|---|---|---|---|



**STEP 1** Find the relationship between the units.

Meters are __3__ powers of 10 smaller than kilometers.

There are __1000__ meters in 1 kilometer.

**STEP 2** Determine the operation to be used.

I am converting from a __smaller__ unit to a __larger__ unit, so I will __divide__.

**STEP 3** Convert.

| number of meters | | meters in 1 kilometer | | number of kilometers |
|---|---|---|---|---|
| 15,000 | ÷ | 1,000 | = | 15 |

So, Alex's house is __15__ kilometers from his grandparent's house.

**Math Talk** MATHEMATICAL PRACTICES 7 Look for a Pattern Choose two units in the chart. Explain how you use powers of 10 to describe how the two units are related.

Possible units: hectograms and centigrams. Possible explanation: Hectograms are 4 powers of 10 larger than centigrams, or centigrams are 4 powers of 10 smaller than hectograms.





---

## Reteach 10.5 RtI

Name ______________________ Lesson 10.5 Reteach

### Metric Measures

The metric system is based on place value. To convert between units, you multiply or divide by a power of 10. You **multiply** to change larger units to smaller units, such as liters to centiliters. You **divide** to change smaller units to larger units, such as meters to kilometers.

**Convert 566 millimeters to decimeters.**

- Think about how the two units are related.
  1 decimeter = 100 millimeters
- **Think:** Should I multiply or divide?
  Millimeters are smaller than decimeters.
  So divide, or move the decimal point left for each power of 10.

566 *millimeters* ÷ 100 *mm in 1 dm* = 5.66 *total decimeters*

So, 566 mm = 5.66 dm.

| Metric Units of Length |
|---|
| 1 centimeter (cm) = 10 millimeters (mm) |
| 1 decimeter (dm) = 10 centimeters (cm) |
| 1 meter (m) = 1,000 millimeters (mm) |
| 1 kilometer (km) = 1,000 meters (m) |

| | | | | 5 | . 6 | 6 |
|---|---|---|---|---|---|---|
| kilo- (k) | hecto- (h) | deka- (da) | meter liter gram | deci- (d) | centi- (c) | milli- (m) |

**Complete the equation to show the conversion.**

1. 115 km × 10 = 1,150 hm
   115 km × 100 = 11,500 dam
   115 km × 1,000 = 115,000 m
2. 418 cL ÷ 10 = 41.8 dL
   418 cL ÷ 100 = 4.18 L
   418 cL ÷ 1,000 = 0.418 daL

**Convert.**

3. 40 cm = 400 mm
4. 500 mL = 5, or 5.00 dL
5. 6 kg = 6,000 g
6. 5,000 cL = 50, or 50.00 L
7. 4 kg = 40 hg
8. 200 mm = 20, or 20.0 cm

Chapter Resources © Houghton Mifflin Harcourt Publishing Company 10-13 Reteach

---

## Enrich 10.5 Differentiated Instruction

Name ______________________ Lesson 10.5 Enrich

### Metric Maze

**Katie, Eldon, and Marco are taking different paths through the Metric Maze below. Follow each of their paths, and add to find the total distance each person travels. Then answer the questions below.**

| Metric Units of Length |
|---|
| 1 meter (m) = 10 decimeters (dm) |
| 1 dm = 10 centimeters (cm) |
| 1 cm = 10 millimeters (mm) |

STARTING LINE

Katie: 750 cm, 15 m, 600 cm, 90 dm, 3 m
Eldon: 11 m, 425 cm, 2,500 mm, 60 dm, 1,100 cm
Marco: 100 dm, 8 m, 42 dm, 1,000 cm, 300 cm

FINISH LINE

1. Who has the shortest path to the Finish Line? Eldon
2. Who has the longest path to the Finish Line? Katie
3. Write Math **Explain** how you changed the units so that you could compare the lengths of the paths.
   Possible explanation: I multiplied or divided to change all the units to centimeters. Then I found the sum of each path's measurements so that I could compare total lengths.

Chapter Resources © Houghton Mifflin Harcourt Publishing Company 10-14 Enrich

## Another Way Use a diagram.

Jamie made a bracelet 1.8 decimeters long. How many millimeters long is Jamie's bracelet?

**Convert 1.8 decimeters to millimeters.**

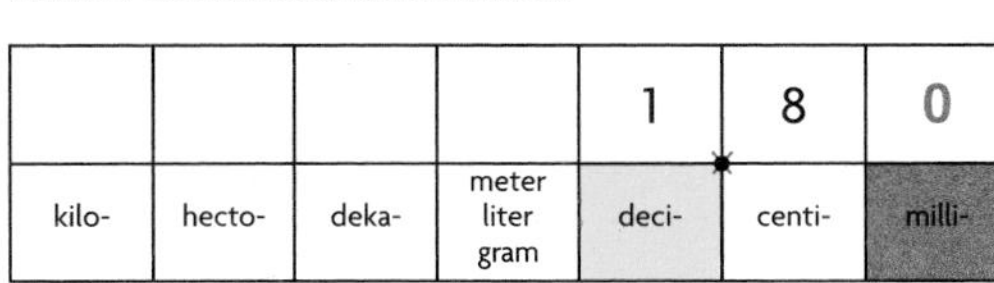

| | | | | 1 | 8 | 0 |
|---|---|---|---|---|---|---|
| kilo- | hecto- | deka- | meter liter gram | deci- | centi- | milli- |

**STEP 1** Show 1.8 decimeters.

Since the unit is decimeters, place the decimal point to show decimeters as the unit.

**STEP 2** Convert.

Cross out the decimal point and place it to show millimeters as the unit. Write zeros to the left of the decimal point as needed.

**STEP 3** Record the value with the new units.

1.8 dm = 180 mm

So, Jamie's bracelet is 180 millimeters long.

**Try This!** **Complete the equation to show the conversion.**

**A** Convert 247 milligrams to centigrams, decigrams, and grams.

Are the units being converted to a larger unit or a smaller unit? larger

Should you multiply or divide by powers of 10 to convert? divide

247 mg (÷) 10 = 24.7 cg

247 mg (÷) 100 = 2.47 dg

247 mg (÷) 1,000 = 0.247 g

**B** Convert 3.9 hectoliters to dekaliters, liters, and deciliters.

Are the units being converted to a larger unit or a smaller unit? smaller

Should you multiply or divide by powers of 10 to convert? multiply

3.9 hL (×) 10 = 39 daL

3.9 hL (×) 100 = 390 L

3.9 hL (×) 1,000 = 3,900 dL





## Advanced Learners

Visual
Individual

**Materials** almanacs, Internet, sports reference books

- Metric measures are used in Olympic games. For example, the Olympics use a 50-m swimming pool and include a 1-km relay race and a 5,000-m speed skating race.
- **How does a 5,000-m race compare with a 10-km race? Explain how you know.** 5,000 m is half of 10 km. 10 km = 10,000 m; 10,000 ÷ 2 = 5,000
- Write and complete other comparisons by changing the units of the races described above. Then have students look up other distances in Olympic events and write and complete similar comparisons.

## Another Way

**MP4 Model with mathematics.** If students have difficulty understanding the placement of the decimal, have them do the following as they complete Steps 1 and 2:

- **Step 1** Recognize that decimeters are the units, so the decimeter unit box is shaded. The decimal point is placed at the upper-right corner of the box to signify the unit, or ones position.
- **Step 2** So that students correctly identify where to place the new decimal point, have them shade the desired unit box (in this case millimeter) and place the decimal point at the upper-right corner of the box. Make sure they see that they will need to write a zero to show the quantity as millimeters.

## Try This!

These examples provide opportunities for students to decide whether they must multiply or divide to convert between given metric units, and to complete the conversions. Students should recognize that converting to a larger unit requires division and converting to a smaller unit requires multiplication.

You may want to give students additional practice in converting metric measures by using an activity found in *i*Tools: Measurement • Equivalent Measures • Weight/Mass; Capacity. *i*Tools can be found at *www.thinkcentral.com*.

## COMMON ERRORS

**Error** Students multiply to change a smaller unit to a larger unit.

**Example** 1 cm = 100 m

**Springboard to Learning** Display a meterstick and have students note that it represents 1 meter, as well as 100 centimeters.

Write 100 cm = ___ m on the board. Have students say the unknown value, 1, and discuss why multiplication is not used to find the answer. Then lead students to generalize that we use division to change a smaller unit (such as centimeters) to a larger unit (such as meters).

## 3 EXPLAIN

### Share and Show

The first problem connects to the learning model. Have students use the MathBoard to explain their thinking.

Use the checked exercises for **Quick Check**. Students should show their answers for Quick Check on the MathBoards.

Use **Math Talk** to focus on students' understanding of metric comparisons.

- **Could you also use the same method to compare 5,000 km and 5,000 m?** Yes. As long as the numbers are equal, I can compare the units. I know that kilometers are longer than meters, so 5,000 km is longer than 5,000 m.

### Quick Check

**If** a student misses the checked exercises

**Then** Differentiate Instruction with
- Reteach 10.5
- Personal Math Trainer 5.MD.A.1
- RtI Tier 1 Activity (online)

### On Your Own

Encourage students to use the table on page 611 for converting. For each conversion, students should locate the two units in the table. Then they should use multiplication when converting to a smaller unit or division when converting to a larger unit.

**MP2 Reason abstractly and quantitatively.** Exercise 12 requires students to extend what they have learned by converting to metric units that are 6 powers of 10 smaller.

---

Name ________________

### Share and Show

**Complete the equation to show the conversion.**

1. 8.47 L (×) 10 = 84.7 dL
   8.47 L (×) 100 = 847 cL
   8.47 L (×) 1,000 = 8,470 mL

Think: Are the units being converted to a larger unit or a smaller unit?

2. 9,824 dg (÷) 10 = 982.4 g
   9,824 dg (÷) 100 = 98.24 dag
   9,824 dg (÷) 1,000 = 9.824 hg

**Convert.**

3. 4,250 cm = 42.5 m
4. 6,000 mL = 6 L
5. 4 dg = 40 cg

MATHEMATICAL PRACTICES 2

Reason Quantitatively How can you compare the lengths 4.25 dm and 4.25 cm without converting?

Possible explanation: The numbers are equal. So, I can compare the units. Decimeters are longer than centimeters. So, 4.25 dm is longer than 4.25 cm.

### On Your Own

**Convert.**

6. 7 g = 7,000 mg
7. 5 km = 5,000 m
8. 1,521 mL = 15.21 dL

**Compare. Write >, <, or =.**

9. 32 hg (=) 3.2 kg
10. 6 km (>) 660 m
11. 525 mL (<) 525 cL

12. MATHEMATICAL PRACTICE 2 **Use Reasoning** Are there less than 1 million, exactly 1 million, or greater than 1 million milligrams in 1 kilogram? Explain how you know.

exactly 1 million; Possible explanation: I used the table: Kilograms are 6 powers of 10 larger than milligrams. So, there are $10^6$, or 1,000,000 milligrams, in a kilogram.

13. GO DEEPER Parker ran 100 meters, 1 kilometer, and 5,000 centimeters. How many meters did he run all together?

1,150 meters

MATHEMATICAL PRACTICES ANALYZE • LOOK FOR STRUCTURE • PRECISION

## Problem Solving • Applications

For 14–15, use the table.

| Food for Camping | |
|---|---|
| Item | Amount |
| 1 can of juice | 150 mL |
| 1 bottle of juice | 2 L |
| 1 batch of pancakes | 200 g |
| raisin & pretzel snack mix | 1,425 g |

14. GO DEEPER Kelly made one batch of raisin and pretzel snack mix. How many grams does she need to add to the snack mix to make 2 kilograms?

575 grams

15. THINK SMARTER Kelly plans to take juice on her camping trip. Which will hold more juice, 8 cans or 2 bottles? How much more?

2 bottles; 2,800 mL

WRITE Math
Show Your Work

16. Erin's water bottle holds 600 milliliters of water. Dylan's water bottle holds 1 liter of water. Whose water bottle holds more water? How much more water?

Dylan's; 400 mL

17. Liz and Alana each participated in the high jump at the track meet. Liz's high jump was 1 meter. Alana's high jump was 132 centimeters. Who jumped higher? How much higher?

Alana; 32 cm

18. THINK SMARTER Monica has 426 millimeters of fabric. How many centimeters of fabric does Monica have? Use the numbers and symbols on the tiles to write an equation to show the conversion.

| 426 | 4.26 | 42.6 | 0.426 |
|---|---|---|---|
| × | ÷ | = | |
| 10 | 100 | 1,000 | |

$426 \div 10 = 42.6$

## DIFFERENTIATED INSTRUCTION | INDEPENDENT ACTIVITIES

Differentiated Centers Kit

*Activities*
*Conversion Challenge*

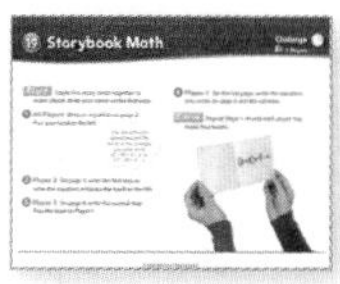

Students complete purple Activity Card 2 by converting among metric units of length.

*Literature*
*A Math Mix-Up*

Students read about a mix-up in customary and metric measurements that led to the NASA's Mars Climate Orbiter crashing into Mars.

*Games*
*2 Steps Forward, 1 Step Back*

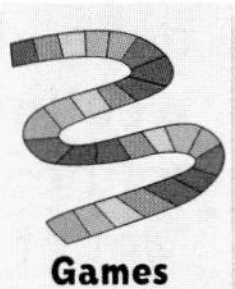


Students convert customary and metric units to move along the game path.

# 4 ELABORATE

## Problem Solving • Applications

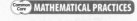

MATHEMATICAL PRACTICES

THINK SMARTER

Make sure students understand that they're looking for answers to two questions.

### Math on the Spot Video Tutor

Use this video to help students model and solve this type of *Think Smarter* problem.

**Math on the Spot** videos are in the Interactive Student Edition and at *www.thinkcentral.com*.

In Problems 16 and 17, challenge your advanced learners to explain how to find the answers using only mental math.

THINK SMARTER

Problem 18 assesses a student's ability to solve a problem that involves conversion of metric units, in this case, millimeters to centimeters. A student who writes the equation $42.6 \times 10 = 426$ may understand that the number of millimeters and centimeters differ by a factor of 10, but does not understand that the answer to the equation should be the number of centimeters. If students choose division but by the wrong power of 10, they may not understand the relative magnitude of metric units.

# 5 EVALUATE Formative Assessment

## Essential Question

### Using the Language Objective

**Reflect** Have students use a sports example to answer the essential question.

**How can you compare and convert metric units?** Possible answer: I have to decide if I am converting a smaller unit to a larger unit, or a larger unit to a smaller unit. Once I know that, I convert by multiplying or dividing by the appropriate power of ten.

## Math Journal WRITE Math

**Explain the relationship between multiplying and dividing by 10, 100, and 1,000 and moving the decimal point to the right or to the left.**

## Practice and Homework

Use the Practice and Homework pages to provide students with more practice of the concepts and skills presented in this lesson. Students master their understanding as they complete practice items and then challenge their critical thinking skills with Problem Solving. Use the Write Math section to determine student's understanding of content for this lesson. Encourage students to use their Math Journals to record their answers.

Practice and Homework
Lesson 10.5

Name ____________

**Metric Measures**

COMMON CORE STANDARD—5.MD.A.1 *Convert like measurement units within a given measurement system.*

**Convert.**

1. 16 m = 16,000 mm
   number of meters × millimeters in 1 meter = number of millimeters
   16 × 1,000 = 16,000
   16 m = 16,000 mm
2. 6,500 cL = 65 L
3. 15 cm = 150 mm
4. 3,200 g = 3.2 kg
5. 12 L = 12,000 mL
6. 200 cm = 2 m
7. 70,000 g = 70 kg
8. 100 dL = 10 L
9. 60 m = 60,000 mm

**Compare. Write <, >, or =.**

10. 900 cm (=) 9,000 mm
11. 600 km (>) 5 m
12. 5,000 cm (>) 5 m
13. 18,000 g (>) 10 kg
14. 8,456 mL (<) 9 L
15. 2 m (<) 275 cm

**Problem Solving** Real World

16. Bria ordered 145 centimeters of fabric. Jayleen ordered 1.5 meters of fabric. Who ordered more fabric?
    Jayleen
17. Ed fills his sports bottle with 1.2 liters of water. After his bike ride, he drinks 200 milliliters of the water. How much water is left in Ed's sports bottle?
    1 L, or 1,000 mL
18. WRITE Math Explain the relationship between multiplying and dividing by 10, 100, and 1,000 and moving the decimal point to the right or to the left.
    Check students' explanations.





## Cross-Curricular

### SCIENCE

- Earth and its moon have a lot in common, but they also have some differences. Both are made from the same elements, both have craters, and both are rocky. Earth is much larger than its moon, and has a greater pull of gravity. The diameter of the moon is about 3,476 km; the diameter of Earth is about 12,700 km.
- What are the diameters of Earth and its moon in meters?
  Earth: 12,700,000 m; Moon: 3,476,000 m

### SOCIAL STUDIES

- Mount Denali, part of the Alaska Range chain of mountains, is the highest point in North America. Its name is fitting because *Denali* means "the high one" in Athabaskan dialect. Its peak reaches an altitude of 6,194 meters. It can take anywhere from 14 days to 5 weeks, depending on the weather, to climb to the summit of Mount Denali.
- How tall is Mount Denali in kilometers? 6.194 km

## Lesson Check (5.MD.A.1)

1. Quan bought 8.6 meters of fabric. How many centimeters of fabric did he buy?

   860 centimeters

2. Jason takes 2 centiliters of medicine. How many milliliters is this?

   20 milliliters

## Spiral Review (5.NF.A.1, 5.MD.A.1, 5.G.A.1)

3. Yolanda needs 5 pounds of ground beef to make lasagna for a family reunion. One package of ground beef weighs $2\frac{1}{2}$ pounds. Another package weighs $2\frac{3}{5}$ pounds. How much ground beef will Yolanda have left over after making the lasagna?

   $\frac{1}{10}$ pound

4. A soup recipe calls for $2\frac{3}{4}$ quarts of vegetable broth. An open can of broth contains $\frac{1}{2}$ quart of broth. How much more broth do you need to make the soup?

   $2\frac{1}{4}$ quarts

5. Which point on the graph is located at (4, 2)?

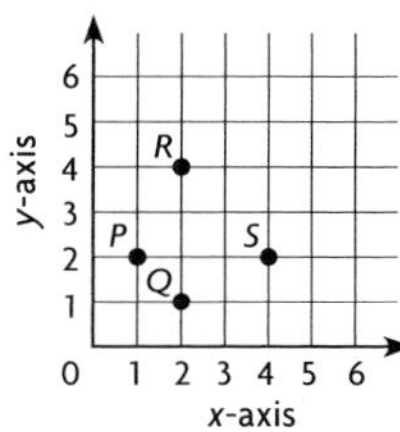


   S

6. A bakery supplier receives an order for 2 tons of flour from a bakery chain. The flour is shipped in crates. Each crate holds eight 10-pound bags of flour. How many crates does the supplier need to ship to fulfill the order?

   50 crates

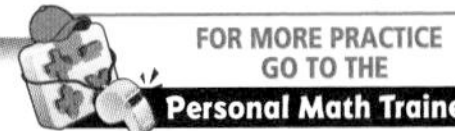






Continue concepts and skills practice with Lesson Check. Use Spiral Review to engage students in previously taught concepts and to promote content retention. Common Core standards are correlated to each section.

LESSON 10.6

# Problem Solving • Customary and Metric Conversions

FOCUS COHERENCE RIGOR

## LESSON AT A GLANCE

### F C R Focus:

**Common Core State Standards**

**5.MD.A.1** Convert among different-sized standard measurement units within a given measurement system (e.g., convert 5 cm to 0.05 m), and use these conversions in solving multi-step, real world problems.

**MATHEMATICAL PRACTICES**

**MP2** Reason abstractly and quantitatively. **MP3** Construct viable arguments and critique the reasoning of others. **MP4** Model with mathematics. **MP7** Look for and make use of structure.

### F C R Coherence:

**Standards Across the Grades**

| **Before** | **Grade 5** | **After** |
|---|---|---|
| 4.MD.A.1 | 5.MD.A.1 | 6.RP.A.3d |

### F C R Rigor:

**Level 1: Understand Concepts**....................*Share and Show* (✓ Checked Items)
**Level 2: Procedural Skills and Fluency**.......*On Your Own*
**Level 3: Applications**.................................*Think Smarter and Go Deeper*

### Learning Objective

Solve problems about customary and metric conversions using the strategy *make a table.*

### Language Objective

Students find an example in the lesson to explain how you can use the strategy *make a table* to help solve problems about customary and metric conversions.

### Materials

MathBoard

F C R For more about how *GO Math!* fosters **Coherence** within the Content Standards and Mathematical Progressions for this chapter, see page 583J.

## About the Math

**Professional Development**

### Modeling Measurement Conversions

In their work in this chapter, students have applied the fundamental rules of measurement conversion in a variety of contexts. Nevertheless, students may continue to have difficulty making conversions because, in the abstract, the rules may continue to seem contradictory:

- *Multiply* if you are converting to a *smaller* unit.
- *Divide* if you are converting to a *larger* unit.

To master measurement conversion, students must be able to order units by size–for example, *inch, foot, yard,* and *mile* for customary units of length. Once they can do that, a model can clear up the apparently contradictory nature of the conversion rules. Modeling helps students visualize the process, showing that converting to a smaller unit produces more units, while converting to a larger unit produces fewer.

**Professional Development Videos**

**Measurement Conversion to a Smaller Unit**

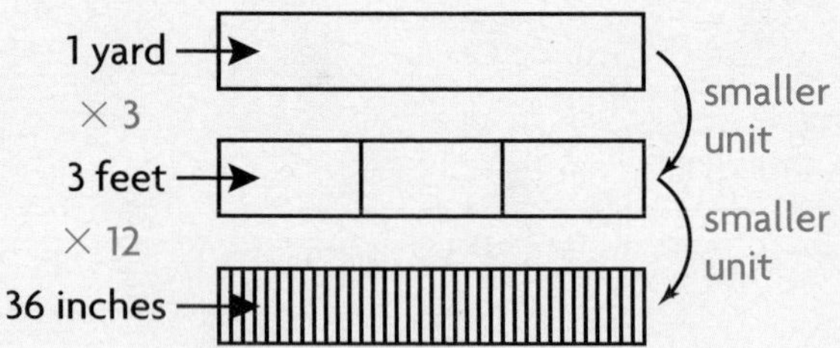


**Measurement Conversion to a Larger Unit**

16 cups ÷ 4 = 4 quarts ÷ 4 = 1 gallon

larger unit

larger unit

## Daily Routines

Common Core

### Problem of the Day 10.6

A dairy cow drank 36 gallons of water in a day. At that rate, how many quarts of water did the cow drink in 1 hour? 6 quarts

### Vocabulary

GO DIGITAL
- Interactive Student Edition
- Multimedia eGlossary

## Fluency Builder

**Skills Practice** Have students use the following chart to convert units of length.

| Customary Units of Length |
|---|
| 1 foot (ft) = 12 inches (in.) |
| 1 yard (yd) = 3 ft |
| 1 mile (mi) = 5,280 ft |
| 1 mile = 1,760 yd |

| | | | |
|---|---|---|---|
| 1. 8 feet | = | 96 | inches |
| 2. 21,120 feet | = | 4 | miles |
| 3. 328 yards | = | 984 | feet |
| 4. 10 miles | = | 17,600 | yards |
| 5. 288 inches | = | 24 | feet |
| 6. 59,840 yards | = | 34 | miles |

# 1 ENGAGE

### with the Interactive Student Edition

## Essential Question

How can you use the strategy *make a table* to help you solve problems about customary and metric conversions?

## Making Connections

Invite students to tell you what they know about running contests.

**Have you ever run in a distance contest? How far did you run? Who ran the farthest? What information helped you find out who ran the farthest?** measuring the distance

## Learning Activity

What is the problem the students are trying to solve? Connect the story to the problem.

- **What are you trying to find out?** which beetle ran the farthest
- **How far did the first beetle run?** 2.9 meters
- **How far did the second beetle run?** 265 centimeters
- **How far did the third beetle run?** 2,800 millimeters

## Literacy and Mathematics

Choose one or more of the following activities.

- Have students rewrite the problem using different distances. Have them discuss with a partner how the problem would change.
- Ask students to write a comic strip illustrating the results of the beetle race. Have them share their comic strips with the class.

# 2 EXPLORE

**Common Core** **5.MD.A.1** Convert among different-sized standard measurement units within a given measurement system (e.g., convert 5 cm to 0.05 m), and use these conversions in solving multi-step, real world problems.

## Unlock the Problem

MATHEMATICAL PRACTICES

**MP7 Look for and make use of structure.** Ask questions to be sure students understand how to use the conversion table. Remind students in previous lessons they used division with whole numbers to convert a smaller unit to a larger unit. In this lesson, they will multiply by a fraction to convert a smaller unit to a larger unit.

- **How many quarts are there in 1 pint? Explain your answer.** There is $\frac{1}{2}$ of a quart in 1 pint. Find "1 pt" in the left column. From there, move right to the entry beneath "qt" in the top row: $\frac{1}{2}$.
- **What is the meaning of the number 16 in the top row?** Possible answer: There are 16 cups in 1 gallon.

Point out to students that the table will help them find the information they need to solve the problem. Help them to see that once they know that 1 cup is $\frac{1}{16}$ of a gallon, they can find the total capacity of any number of cups by multiplying the number by $\frac{1}{16}$.

**MP4 Model with mathematics.** If Aaron made enough punch to fill the last gallon container, how many more cups would he be able to fill? 8 cups. He would be making $\frac{1}{2}$ gallon more, and there are 8 cups in a $\frac{1}{2}$ gallon.

## ELL Strategy:

### Rephrase

Organize groups of three or four students.

- Have groups talk about how to convert pints into gallons.
- Write these sentence frames on the board and have students complete them to rephrase how to convert pints into gallons:

  **First, divide the number of** __pints__ **by** __2__ **to get the number of** __quarts__.

  **Then, divide the number of** __quarts__ **by** __4__ **to get the number of** __gallons__.

- Invite volunteers to tell how to convert pints into gallons.



---

Name ______________________

**PROBLEM SOLVING**
**Lesson 10.6**

## Problem Solving • Customary and Metric Conversions

**Measurement and Data—5.MD.A.1**
MATHEMATICAL PRACTICES
**MP2, MP3, MP4, MP7**

**Essential Question** How can you use the strategy *make a table* to help you solve problems about customary and metric conversions?

### Unlock the Problem

Aaron is making fruit punch for a family reunion. He needs to make 120 cups of punch. If he wants to store the fruit punch in gallon containers, how many gallon containers will Aaron need?

Use the graphic organizer below to help you solve the problem.

**Conversion Table**

| | gal | qt | pt | c |
|---|---|---|---|---|
| **1 gal** | 1 | 4 | 8 | 16 |
| **1 qt** | $\frac{1}{4}$ | 1 | 2 | 4 |
| **1 pt** | $\frac{1}{8}$ | $\frac{1}{2}$ | 1 | 2 |
| **1 c** | $\frac{1}{16}$ | $\frac{1}{4}$ | $\frac{1}{2}$ | 1 |

#### Read the Problem

**What do I need to find?**
I need to find __how many gallon containers can be filled with 120 cups of punch__.

**What information do I need to use?**
I need to use __the number of cups being made and the number of cups in 1 gallon__.

**How will I use the information?**
I will make a table to show the relationship between the number of __cups__ and the number of __gallons__.

#### Solve the Problem

There are __16__ cups in 1 gallon. So, each cup is __$\frac{1}{16}$__ of a gallon. Complete the table below.

| c | 1 | 2 | 3 | 4 | 120 |
|---|---|---|---|---|---|
| gal | $\frac{1}{16}$ | $\frac{1}{8}$ | $\frac{3}{16}$ | $\frac{1}{4}$ | $7\frac{1}{2}$ |

Multiply by __$\frac{1}{16}$__.

So, Aaron needs __8__ gallon containers to store the punch.

- MATHEMATICAL PRACTICE 2 **Use Reasoning** Will all of the gallon containers Aaron uses be filled to capacity? Explain. __No; Possible explanation: the last gallon container will only be $\frac{1}{2}$ full.__





---

## Reteach 10.6

Name ______________________

Lesson 10.6
Reteach

### Problem Solving • Customary and Metric Conversions

You can use the strategy *make a table* to help you solve problems about customary and metric conversions.

Jon's faucet is dripping at the rate of 24 centiliters in a day. How many milliliters of water will have dripped from Jon's faucet in 24 hours?

**Read the Problem**

**What do I need to find?**
I need to find __how many milliliters of water will have dripped from Jon's faucet in 24 hours.__

**What information do I need to use?**
I need to use __the number of cL that have dripped in 24 hr and the number of mL in a cL.__

**How will I use the information?**
I will make a table to show the relationship between the number of __centiliters__ and the number of __milliliters__.

**Conversion Table**

| | L | dL | cL | mL |
|---|---|---|---|---|
| **1 L** | 1 | 10 | 100 | 1,000 |
| **1 dL** | $\frac{1}{10}$ | 1 | 10 | 100 |
| **1 cL** | $\frac{1}{100}$ | $\frac{1}{10}$ | 1 | 10 |
| **1 mL** | $\frac{1}{1,000}$ | $\frac{1}{100}$ | $\frac{1}{10}$ | 1 |

I can use the Conversion Table to find the number of milliliters in 1 centiliter.

There are __10__ milliliters in 1 centiliter.

| cL | 1 | 2 | 4 | 24 |
|---|---|---|---|---|
| mL | 10 | 20 | 40 | 240 |

So, __240__ milliliters of water will have dripped from Jon's faucet in 24 hours.

**Make a table to help you solve the problems.** Check students' tables.

1. Fernando has a bucket that holds 3 gallons of water. He is filling the bucket using a 1-pint container. How many times will he have to fill the pint container in order to fill the bucket?

   __24 times__

2. Lexi has a roll of shelf paper that is 800 cm long. She wants to cut the paper into 1-m strips to line the shelves in her pantry. How many 1-meter strips can she cut?

   __8 strips__




---

## Enrich 10.6

**Differentiated Instruction**

Name ______________________

Lesson 10.6
Enrich

### More Customary Units

**The table below shows customary units of length and capacity that are sometimes used.**

| Units of Length | Units of Capacity |
|---|---|
| 1 rod = 16.5 feet | 1 fluid dram = $\frac{1}{8}$ fluid ounce |
| 1 furlong = 40 rods | 1 gill = 4 fluid ounces |
| 1 mile = 8 furlongs | 1 peck = 8 quarts |
| 1 fathom = 6 feet | 1 bushel = 4 pecks |
| 1 league = 3 miles | 1 tablespoon = $\frac{1}{2}$ fluid ounce |
| | 1 teaspoon = $\frac{1}{3}$ tablespoon |

**Solve.**

1. How many yards are in 1 rod? __5.5 yards__
2. How many feet are in 1 furlong? __660 feet__
3. How many furlongs are in 1,760 yards? __8 furlongs__
4. How many inches are in 1 fathom? __72 inches__
5. How many miles are in 20,000 leagues? __60,000 miles__
6. How many fluid drams are in 1 ounce? __8 fluid drams__
7. How many gills are in 1 pint? __4 gills__
8. How many pints are in 1 peck? __16 pints__
9. How many quarts are in 3 bushels? __96 quarts__
10. How many fluid drams are in 1 gill? __32 fluid drams__
11. How many teaspoons are in 1 tablespoon? __3 teaspoons__
12. How many tablespoons are in 1 gill? __8 tablespoons__
13. Write Math **Explain** how you solved Exercise 12. __Since 1 tablespoon = $\frac{1}{2}$ fluid ounce, 2 tablespoons = 1 fluid ounce. Since 1 gill = 4 fluid ounces, 4 fluid ounces equals 8 tablespoons.__

## Try Another Problem

Sharon is working on a project for art class. She needs to cut strips of wood that are each 1 decimeter long to complete the project. If Sharon has 7 strips of wood that are each 1 meter long, how many 1-decimeter strips can she cut?

**Conversion Table**

| | m | dm | cm | mm |
|---|---|---|---|---|
| 1 m | 1 | 10 | 100 | 1,000 |
| 1 dm | $\frac{1}{10}$ | 1 | 10 | 100 |
| 1 cm | $\frac{1}{100}$ | $\frac{1}{10}$ | 1 | 10 |
| 1 mm | $\frac{1}{1,000}$ | $\frac{1}{100}$ | $\frac{1}{10}$ | 1 |

**Read the Problem**

| What do I need to find? | What information do I need to use? | How will I use the information? |
|---|---|---|
| I need to find how many 1-decimeter lengths of wood Sharon can cut. | I need to use the number of meter strips Sharon has and the number of decimeters in 1 meter. | I will make a table to show the relationship between the number of meters and the number of decimeters. |

**Solve the Problem**

Since 1 meter is equal to 10 decimeters, I can make a table to show the relationship between meters and decimeters. I can use the table to find the number of 1-decimeter strips Sharon can cut.

| m | 1 | 2 | 3 | 4 | 7 |
|---|---|---|---|---|---|
| dm | 10 | 20 | 30 | 40 | 70 |

Multiply by 10.

So, Sharon can cut 70 1-decimeter lengths to complete her project.

- MATHEMATICAL PRACTICE 7 **Look for a Pattern** What relationship did the table you made show? Possible answer: The table shows the relationship between meters and decimeters. 1 meter = 10 decimeters

Math Talk — MATHEMATICAL PRACTICES 4 — Use Diagrams How could you use a diagram to solve this problem?

Possible answer: I could draw a diagram showing 7 rectangles to represent the seven 1-meter strips of wood. Then I would divide each rectangle into 10 equal parts since there are 10 decimeters in a meter. 7 groups of 10 is equal to 70.





## Try Another Problem

After students read the problem, ask:

**MP4 Model with mathematics.**

- **Would you expect the number of 1-decimeter strips that Sharon can cut from the 7 strips of wood to be greater than or less than 7? Why?** greater than; Possible answer: 1 decimeter is 10 times smaller than 1 meter. So, the number of strips she can cut from one 1-meter strip will be greater than 7. The number she can cut from 7 strips will be greater still.

**MP6 Attend to precision.**

After students solve the problem, ask:

- **Explain how the way you solved this problem is different from the way you solved the problem on page 617.** Possible explanation: In the problem on page 617, the given unit is smaller than the unit I converted to, so I used a fraction to show the relationship. For this problem, the given unit is larger than the unit I converted to, so I used a whole number to show the relationship.

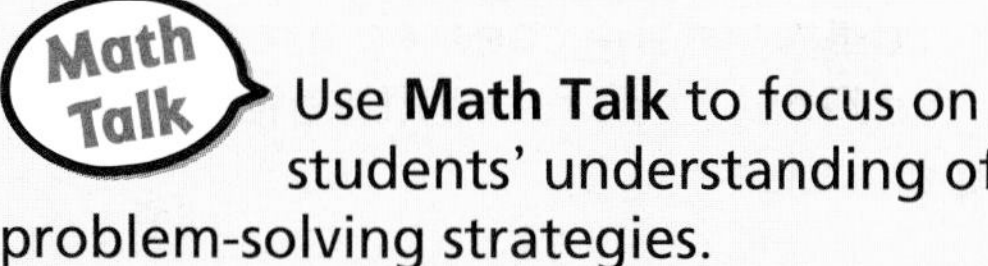


Use **Math Talk** to focus on students' understanding of problem-solving strategies.

- **How could you solve the problem using the powers of 10?** Possible answer: If Sharon has 7 1-meter strips, she has 7m in all. Decimeter is one power of 10 away from meter, so 7m = 70 dm. That means she can cut 70 1-decimeter strips.

You may suggest that students place completed Try Another Problem graphic organizers in their portfolios.

## Advanced Learners

Logical / Mathematical
Individual

Materials rulers

- Have students create length and weight conversion tables like those in the lesson.
- For length conversion, students should draw a table with 5 rows and 5 columns labeled in miles, yards, feet, and inches.

| | mi | yd | ft | in |
|---|---|---|---|---|
| 1 mi | | | | |
| 1 yd | | | | |
| 1 ft | | | | |
| 1 in. | | | | |

- For weight conversion, students should draw a table with 4 rows and 4 columns labeled in tons, pounds, and ounces.

## COMMON ERRORS

**Error** Students read a conversion table incorrectly.

**Example** 1 cup = 16 gallons

**Springboard to Learning** Before students make their conversions, have them jot down the unit they are given, the unit they will be converting to, and whether they will be converting to a larger or a smaller unit. If they are converting to a larger unit, have them note "smaller answer." If they are converting to a smaller unit, have them note "greater answer."

# 3 EXPLAIN

## Share and Show 

The first problem connects to the learning model. Have students use the MathBoard to explain their thinking.

Use the checked exercises for **Quick Check.** Students should show their answers for the **Quick Check** on the MathBoard.

Make sure to point out that students can use the conversion tables shown on the previous pages.

To solve Exercise 2, students must reverse the process they used to solve Exercise 1. There, they moved in the table from the larger unit (gallons) to the smaller unit (quarts). Here they must move from the smaller unit to the larger unit.

If students complete the checked exercises correctly, they may continue with the remaining exercises.

### Quick Check 

**If** a student misses the checked exercises

**Then** Differentiate Instruction with

- Reteach 10.6
- Personal Math Trainer 5.MD.A.1
- RtI Tier 1 Activity (online)



Name ______________________

## Share and Show 

1. Edgardo has a drink cooler that holds 10 gallons of water. He is filling the cooler with a 1-quart container. How many times will he have to fill the quart container to fill the cooler?

**First,** make a table to show the relationship between gallons and quarts. You can use a conversion table to find how many quarts are in a gallon.

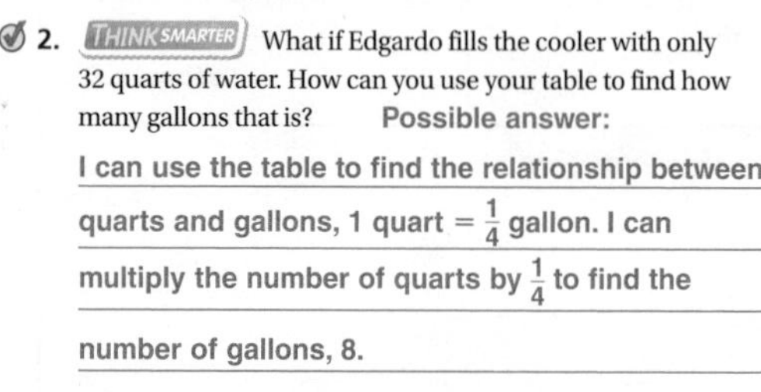

| gal | 1 | 2 | 3 | 4 | 10 |
|---|---|---|---|---|---|
| qt | 4 | 8 | 12 | 16 | 40 |

**Then,** look for a rule to help you complete your table.

number of gallons × __4__ = number of quarts

**Finally,** use the table to solve the problem.

Edgardo will need to fill the quart container __40__ times.

2. THINKSMARTER What if Edgardo fills the cooler with only 32 quarts of water. How can you use your table to find how many gallons that is? Possible answer:

I can use the table to find the relationship between quarts and gallons, 1 quart = $\frac{1}{4}$ gallon. I can multiply the number of quarts by $\frac{1}{4}$ to find the number of gallons, 8.

3. How would the number of times Edgardo uses a container to fill the 10-gallon cooler change if he uses a 1-cup container? Explain.

The number of times he has to fill the container would be greater; Possible explanation: Since there are 4 cups in a quart, Edgardo would have to fill the cup 40 × 4, or 160 times.

WRITE Math • Show Your Work

## On Your Own

4. THINK SMARTER Maria put trim around a banner that is the shape of a triangle. Each side is 22 inches long. Maria has $\frac{1}{2}$ foot of trim left. What was the length of the trim when she started? Write your answer in yards.

2 yards

5. Dan owns 9 DVDs. His brother Mark has 3 more DVDs than Dan has. Their sister, Marsha, has more DVDs than either of her brothers. Together, the three have 35 DVDs. How many DVDs does Marsha have?

Marsha has 14 DVDs.

6. GO DEEPER Kevin is making a picture frame. He has a piece of trim that is 4 feet long. How many 14-inch-long pieces can Kevin cut from the trim? How much of a foot will he have left over?

Kevin can cut three 14-inch-long pieces with half a foot left over.

7. MATHEMATICAL PRACTICE 2 Reason Quantitatively Explain how you could find the number of cups in five gallons of water.

Possible explanation: Since I know that there are 4 quarts in a gallon and 4 cups in a quart, I can multiply the number of gallons by 16 to find the number of cups, 80.

8. Carla uses $2\frac{3}{4}$ cups of whole wheat flour and $1\frac{3}{8}$ cups of rye flour in her bread recipe. How many cups does she use in all?

$4\frac{1}{8}$ cups

9. THINK SMARTER + A large pot holds 12 gallons of soup. Jared has 1-pint containers of chicken broth. Complete the table to help you find the number of 1-pint containers of chicken broth Jared will need to fill the pot.

| gallon | 2 | 4 | 6 | 8 | 10 | 12 |
|---|---|---|---|---|---|---|
| pint | 16 | 32 | 48 | 64 | 80 | 96 |

Jared will need 96 1-pint containers to fill the pot.

## DIFFERENTIATED INSTRUCTION INDEPENDENT ACTIVITIES

**Differentiated Centers Kit**

***Activities***
***Measurement MATHO***

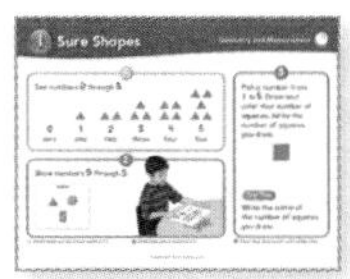

Students complete blue Activity Card 2 by choosing an appropriate metric unit for finding the length, mass, or capacity of an object.

***Literature***
***A Math Mix-Up***

Students read about a mix-up in customary and metric measurements that led to the NASA's Mars Climate Orbiter crashing into Mars.

***Games***
***2 Steps Forward, 1 Step Back***

Students convert customary and metric units to move along the game path.

# 4 ELABORATE

## On Your Own

THINK SMARTER

In Problem 4, students must convert feet to inches, find the total number of inches, and then convert to yards.

### Math on the Spot Video Tutor

Use this video to help students model and solve this type of *Think Smarter* problem.

**Math on the Spot** videos are in the Interactive Student Edition and at *www.thinkcentral.com*.

GO DEEPER

In Problem 6, students must convert 4 feet to inches, then note that after three 14-inch sections are cut from the 48-inch piece, 6 inches, or half a foot, are left over

THINK SMARTER

Item 9 assesses a student's ability to solve problems involving conversion of units of measure by making a table to help. In this item, students convert from gallons to pints. A student who fills in the table with the numbers 8, 16, 24, 32, 40, and 48 may not have noticed that the number of gallons in the table increases by a factor of 2. Some students may begin the table with 4, mistakenly using the number of quarts in a gallon rather than the number of pints in a gallon.

# 5 EVALUATE Formative Assessment

## Essential Question

**Using the Language Objective:**

**Reflect** Have students find an example in the lesson and then explain it to answer the essential question.

**How can you use the strategy *make a table* to help you solve problems about customary and metric conversions?** Possible answer: Use the table to find the correct conversion factor. Then multiply or divide the given number of units by the conversion factor

## Math Journal WRITE Math

**Explain how you could use the conversion table on page 618 to convert 700 centimeters to meters.**

## Practice and Homework

Use the Practice and Homework pages to provide students with more practice of the concepts and skills presented in this lesson. Students master their understanding as they complete practice items and then challenge their critical thinking skills with Problem Solving. Use the Write Math section to determine student's understanding of content for this lesson. Encourage students to use their Math Journals to record their answers.

Name ______________________

**Problem Solving • Customary and Metric Conversions**

**Practice and Homework Lesson 10.6**

Common Core **COMMON CORE STANDARD—5.MD.A.1** *Convert like measurement units within a given measurement system.*

**Solve each problem by making a table.** Possible tables are given.

1. Thomas is making soup. His soup pot holds 8 quarts of soup. How many 1-cup servings of soup will Thomas make?

32 1-cup servings

| Number of Quarts | 1 | 2 | 3 | 4 | 8 |
|---|---|---|---|---|---|
| Number of Cups | 4 | 8 | 12 | 16 | 32 |

2. Paulina works out with a 2.5-kilogram mass. What is the mass of the 2.5-kilogram mass in grams?

2,500 grams

| Number of Kilograms | 1 | 2 | 2.5 |
|---|---|---|---|
| Number of Grams | 1,000 | 2,000 | 2,500 |

3. Alex lives 500 yards from the park. How many inches does Alex live from the park?

18,000 inches

| Yards | 1 | 2 | 3 | 4 | 5 | 500 |
|---|---|---|---|---|---|---|
| Inches | 36 | 72 | 108 | 144 | 180 | 18,000 |

4. A flatbed truck is loaded with 7,000 pounds of bricks. How many tons of brick are on the truck?

3.5 tons

| Pounds | 2,000 | 3,000 | 4,000 | 7,000 |
|---|---|---|---|---|
| Tons | 1 | 1.5 | 2 | 3.5 |

5. WRITE Math Explain how you could use the conversion table on page 618 to convert 700 centimeters to meters.

Check students' explanations.

## Mathematical Practices in Your Classroom

### CCSS.Math.Practice.MP7 Look for and make use of structure.

At its simplest, a table is a repository of data. Referring to it, we can find information that we can apply to some useful purpose. By understanding the logic of the table, we may be able to put it to greater use, analyzing its structure to find patterns and rules we can use to calculate data that are not contained in the table. For example, we can use tables to discover information about customary units of capacity that the table does not show.

Ask questions such as the following to help students see the structure of the table on page 617:

- **What pattern do you see in the number of quarts, pints, and cups in the top row?** The number of pints is twice the number of quarts and half the number of cups.
- **How could you use that information to find the number of quarts and the number of cups that are equivalent to 14 pints?** The number of quarts would be half the number of pints, or 7. The number of cups would be twice the number of pints, or 28.
- **How does the table show the relationship between the number of gallons in a measurement and the number of cups?** The table shows that 1 gallon is 16 times as large as 1 cup, or that 1 cup is $\frac{1}{16}$ of 1 gallon.

## Lesson Check (5.MD.A.1)

1. At the hairdresser, Jenny had 27 centimeters cut off her hair. How many decimeters of hair did Jenny have cut off?

2.7 dm

2. Marcus needs 108 inches of wood to make a frame. How many feet of wood does Marcus need for the frame?

9 feet

## Spiral Review (5.NF.B.7c, 5.MD.A.1, 5.G.A.1)

3. Tara lives 35,000 meters from her grandparents. How many kilometers does Tara live from her grandparents?

35 km

4. Dane's puppy weighed 8 ounces when it was born. Now the puppy weighs 18 times as much as it did when it was born. How many pounds does Dane's puppy weigh now?

9 pounds

5. A carpenter is cutting dowels from a piece of wood that is 10 inches long. How many $\frac{1}{2}$-inch dowels can the carpenter cut?

20 dowels

6. What ordered pair describes the location of point $X$?

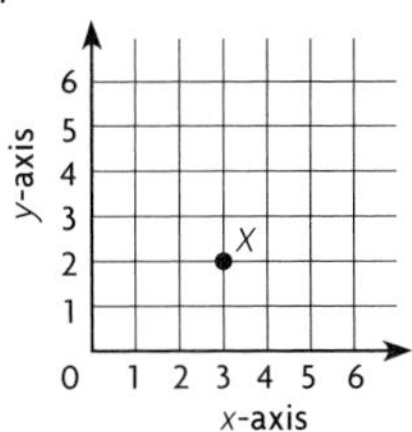


(3, 2)

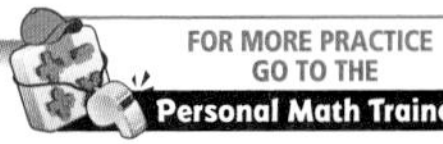






Continue concepts and skills practice with Lesson Check. Use Spiral Review to engage students in previously taught concepts and to promote content retention. Common Core standards are correlated to each section.

LESSON 10.7

# Elapsed Time

FOCUS COHERENCE RIGOR

## LESSON AT A GLANCE

### F C R Focus:

**Common Core State Standards**

**5.MD.A.1** Convert among different-sized standard measurement units within a given measurement system (e.g., convert 5 cm to 0.05 m), and use these conversions in solving multi-step, real world problems.

**MATHEMATICAL PRACTICES**

**MP6** Attend to precision. **MP7** Look for and make use of structure.

### F C R Coherence:

**Standards Across the Grades**

| Before | Grade 5 | After |
|---|---|---|
| 4.MD.A.1 | 5.MD.A.1 | 6.RP.A.3d |

### F C R Rigor:

**Level 1: Understand Concepts**..................*Share and Show* (✓ Checked Items)
**Level 2: Procedural Skills and Fluency**.......*On Your Own*
**Level 3: Applications**...............................*Think Smarter and Go Deeper*

### Learning Objective

Convert units of time to solve elapsed time problems.

### Language Objective

Students discuss how you can solve elapsed time problems by converting units of time.

### Materials

MathBoard

F C R For more about how *GO Math!* fosters **Coherence** within the Content Standards and Mathematical Progressions for this chapter, see page 583J.

## About the Math

**Professional Development**

### Why Teach This

Converting and comparing units of time is not only a math skill, but an everyday life skill. Students are likely to find countless opportunities in their lives to use skills learned in this lesson.

Display the *Units of Time* conversion chart, from page 623, in your classroom for easy reference.

To convert units of time, students should continue to reinforce the importance of the generalization that we use multiplication to change a larger unit of time to a smaller unit of time and division to change a smaller unit of time to a larger unit of time.

**Professional Development Videos**

**Personal Math Trainer**

**Math on the Spot**

**Animated Math Models**

*i*T *i*Tools: Measurement

**HMH Mega Math**

# Daily Routines

Common Core

## Problem of the Day 10.7

Deanna used 2.5 deciliters of milk in a recipe. How many milliliters of milk did Deanna use? 250 milliliters

### Vocabulary

- Interactive Student Edition
- Multimedia *e*Glossary

## Fluency Builder

**Skills Practice** Have students use the following chart to convert units of capacity. Remind students that sometimes they may need to convert more than once.

| Customary Units of Capacity |
|---|
| 1 cup (c) = 8 fluid ounces (fl oz) |
| 1 pint (pt) = 2 cups |
| 1 quart (qt) = 2 pints |
| 1 gallon (gal) = 4 quarts |

| | | | |
|---|---|---|---|
| 1. 512 cups | = | 4,096 | fluid ounces |
| 2. 45 gallons | = | 180 | quarts |
| 3. 11,824 fluid ounces | = | 1,478 | cups |
| 4. 728 pints | = | 91 | gallons |
| 5. 136 quarts | = | 544 | cups |
| 6. 9,840 fluid ounces | = | 615 | pints |

# 1 ENGAGE

with the Interactive Student Edition

## Essential Question

How can you solve elapsed time problems by converting units of time?

## Making Connections

Ask students to tell what they know about units of time.

**What are all the units of time you can name?** Possible answers: seconds, minutes, hours, days, weeks, months, years **How are these units related?** Possible answers: 60 seconds in 1 minute; 60 minutes in 1 hour; 24 hours in 1 day; 7 days in 1 week; 12 months in 1 year

## Learning Activity

What is the problem the students are trying to solve? Connect the story to the problem. Ask the following questions.

- **How can you compare amounts of time if they are in different units?** Convert one of the measurements so that both amounts are in the same units.
- **If you are comparing amounts of time in different units, how do you decide which unit to convert?** Possible answer: Convert the larger unit to the smaller unit.

## Literacy and Mathematics

View the lesson opener with the students. Then, ask students to calculate how many days old they are. Have students share their results and explain their method of calculation in writing.

# 2 EXPLORE

## Unlock the Problem

MATHEMATICAL PRACTICES

**MP6 Attend to precision.** If your classroom does not have an analog clock, sketch an analog clock face on the board.

Discuss the problem. Have students note that we are being asked to convert a smaller unit (minutes) to a larger unit (hours). Discuss the solution.

- **When we convert from a smaller unit of measure to a larger unit of measure, how does the number of units change?** The number of units decreases.
- **Which operation—multiplication or division—do we use to change to a larger unit of measure?** division

After you discuss the solution, ask:

**MP4 Model with mathematics.**

- **The remainder of the division is 20. Why does 20 represent minutes?** Since you are dividing by 60, the number of minutes in 1 hour, the remainder represents parts (or sixtieths) of 1 hour, which are minutes.

## Try This!

**MP6 Attend to precision.**

- **How is this problem similar to the computer problem?** Possible answer: Similar: I am converting from a smaller unit (days) to a larger mixed unit (weeks and days). Different: I am using different units. So, I divide by 7 rather than 60.

## Strategy:

Scaffold Language

Read the problem. **A train leaves the station at 2:15 P.M. and arrives at the next station at 4:25 P.M. How long was the train ride?**

- Provide these sentence frames to help students make sense of the problem:

**From** 2:15 **to** 3:15 **is one hour.**

**From** 3:15 **to** 4:15 **is one hour.**

**From** 4:15 **to** 4:25 **is** 10 **minutes.**

**The trip lasted** 2 **hours and** 10 **minutes.**

- Repeat, using different times. Have students use the sentence frames to explain how they solved the problem.

**5.MD.A.1** Convert among different-sized standard measurement units within a given measurement system (e.g., convert 5 cm to 0.05m), and use these conversions in solving multi-step, real world problems.

Lesson 10.7

Name ______

## Elapsed Time

**Essential Question** How can you solve elapsed time problems by converting units of time?

Common Core **Measurement and Data—5.MD.A.1**
**MATHEMATICAL PRACTICES MP6, MP7**

### Unlock the Problem (Real World)

A computer company claims its laptop has a battery that lasts 4 hours. The laptop actually ran for 200 minutes before the battery ran out. Did the battery last 4 hours?

1 hour = 60 minutes

**Think:** The minute hand moves from one number to the next in 5 minutes.

**Convert 200 minutes to hours and minutes.**

**STEP 1** Convert minutes into hours and minutes.

200 min = 3 hr 20 min

| total min | | min in 1 hr | | hr | | min |
|---|---|---|---|---|---|---|
| 200 | ÷ | 60 | is | 3 | r | 20 |

**STEP 2** Compare. Write <, >, or =.

3 hr 20 min < 4 hr

Since 3 hours 20 minutes is less than 4 hours, the battery did not last as long as the computer company claims.

**Try This!** **Convert to mixed measures.**

Jill spent much of her summer away from home. She spent 10 days with her grandparents, 9 days with her cousins, and 22 days at camp. How many weeks and days was she away from home?

**STEP 1** Find the total number of days away.

10 days + 9 days + 22 days = 41 days

**STEP 2** Convert the days into weeks and days.

41 ÷ 7 is 5 r 6

So, Jill was away from home 5 weeks and 6 days.

| Units of Time |
|---|
| 60 seconds (s) = 1 minute (min) |
| 60 minutes = 1 hour (hr) |
| 24 hours = 1 day (d) |
| 7 days = 1 week (wk) |
| 52 weeks = 1 year (yr) |
| 12 months (mo) = 1 year |
| 365 days = 1 year |





### Reteach 10.7 RtI

Name ______ Lesson 10.7 Reteach

**Elapsed Time**

You can solve elapsed time problems by converting units of time.

Starting at 4:20 P.M., Connie practiced piano for 90 minutes. At what time did Connie stop practicing piano?

**Convert 90 minutes to hours and minutes. Then find the end time.**

| Units of Time |
|---|
| 60 seconds (s) = 1 minute (min) |
| 60 minutes = 1 hour (hr) |
| 24 hours = 1 day (d) |
| 7 days = 1 week (wk) |
| 52 weeks = 1 year (yr) |
| 12 months (mo) = 1 year |
| 365 days = 1 year |

**Step 1** To convert minutes to hours, divide.
90 ÷ 60 is 1 r 30
90 min = 1 hr 30 min

**Step 2** Count forward by hours until you reach 1 hour. 4:20 → 5:20 = 1 hour

**Step 3** Count forward by minutes until you reach 30 minutes.
5:20 → 5:30 = 1 hour 10 minutes
5:30 → 5:40 = 1 hour 20 minutes
5:40 → 5:50 = 1 hour 30 minutes

Connie stops practicing piano at 5:50 P.M.

**Convert.**

1. 480 min = 8 hr
2. 4 d = 96 hr
3. 125 hr = 5 d 5 hr

**Find the start, elapsed, or end time.**

4. Start time: 7:15 A.M.
Elapsed time: 2 hr 20 min
End time: 9:35 A.M.

5. Start time: 6:28 A.M.
Elapsed time: 3 hr 40 min
End time: 10:08 A.M.

6. Start time: 2:05 P.M.
Elapsed time: 5 hr 50 min
End time: 7:55 P.M.

7. Start time: 5:24 P.M.
Elapsed time: 6 hr
End time: 11:24 P.M.

Chapter Resources 10-17 Reteach
© Houghton Mifflin Harcourt Publishing Company

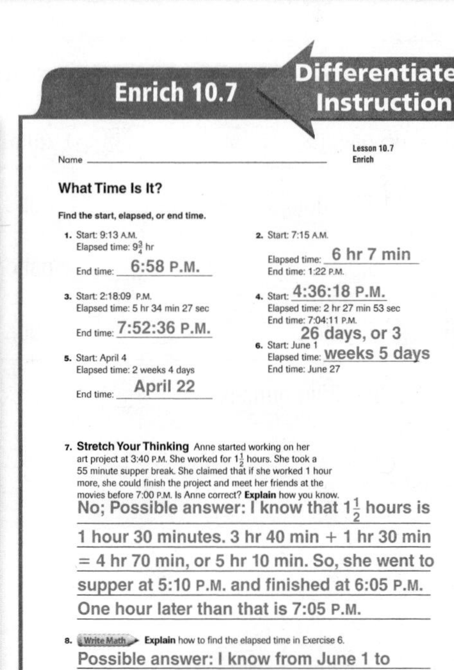

### Enrich 10.7 Differentiated Instruction

Name ______ Lesson 10.7 Enrich

**What Time Is It?**

**Find the start, elapsed, or end time.**

1. Start: 9:13 A.M.
Elapsed time: $9\frac{3}{4}$ hr
End time: 6:58 P.M.

2. Start: 7:15 A.M.
Elapsed time: 6 hr 7 min
End time: 1:22 P.M.

3. Start: 2:18:09 P.M.
Elapsed time: 5 hr 34 min 27 sec
End time: 7:52:36 P.M.

4. Start: 4:36:18 P.M.
Elapsed time: 2 hr 27 min 53 sec
End time: 7:04:11 P.M.

5. Start: April 4
Elapsed time: 2 weeks 4 days
End time: April 22

6. Start: June 1
Elapsed time: 26 days, or 3 weeks 5 days
End time: June 27

7. **Stretch Your Thinking** Anne started working on her art project at 3:40 P.M. She worked for $1\frac{1}{2}$ hours. She took a 55 minute supper break. She claimed that if she worked 1 hour more, she could finish the project and meet her friends at the movies before 7:00 P.M. Is Anne correct? **Explain** how you know.
No; Possible answer: I know that $1\frac{1}{2}$ hours is 1 hour 30 minutes. 3 hr 40 min + 1 hr 30 min = 4 hr 70 min, or 5 hr 10 min. So, she went to supper at 5:10 P.M. and finished at 6:05 P.M. One hour later than that is 7:05 P.M.

8. Write Math **Explain** how to find the elapsed time in Exercise 6.
Possible answer: I know from June 1 to June 27 is 26 days. 26 ÷ 7 is 3 r5, so 26 days = 3 weeks and 5 days.

Chapter Resources 10-18 Enrich
© Houghton Mifflin Harcourt Publishing Company

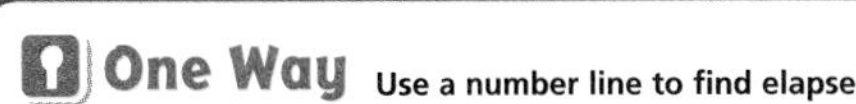

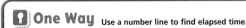

## One Way Use a number line to find elapsed time.

Monica spent $2\frac{1}{2}$ hours working on her computer. If she started working at 10:30 A.M., what time did Monica stop working?

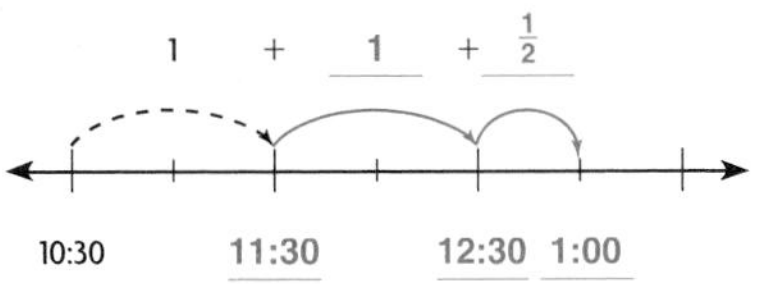


Think: $\frac{1}{2}$ hour = 30 minutes

## Another Way Use a clock to find elapsed time.

Start

End

So, Monica stopped working at 1:00 P.M..

### Try This! Find a start time.

Robert's soccer team needs to be off the soccer field by 12:15 P.M. Each game is at most $1\frac{3}{4}$ hours long. What time should the game begin to be sure that the team finishes on time?

$\frac{1}{4}$ hour = 15 minutes, so $\frac{3}{4}$ hour = 45 minutes

**STEP 1** Subtract the minutes first.

45 minutes earlier is 11:30 A.M..

**STEP 2** Then subtract the hour.

1 hour and 45 minutes earlier is 10:30 A.M..

So, the game should begin at 10:30 A.M..

Possible explanation: I would convert the hours to minutes by multiplying 3 × 60. Then I would add 45 min to 180. So, 3 hr 45 min is equal to 225 min.

**Math Talk** MATHEMATICAL PRACTICES 6

Explain how you could convert 3 hours 45 minutes to minutes.





## One Way

Discuss the example. Make sure students understand that one way to find elapsed time involves finding the starting time on the number line and then counting as they move to the right, until they reach the ending time.

## Another Way

Point out to students that an analog clock face can be thought of as a curved number line. You may want to use an activity in *i*Tools: Measurement to give students additional practice in using analog clocks.

## Try This!

Review fractional units of time, such as half-hour and quarter-hour, before discussing the example.

- **How many minutes are in 1 hour?** 60 minutes
- **How many minutes are in $\frac{1}{2}$ hour?** 30 minutes
- **How many minutes are in $\frac{1}{4}$ hour?** 15 minutes

Use **Math Talk** to focus on students' understanding of mixed units of time.

- Could you also use subtraction instead of addition to make the conversion? Explain. Yes. I could round up and convert 4 hours to minutes by multiplying 4 x 60. Then I can subtract 15 min from 240 to find 225 min.

## Advanced Learners

Visual
Individual

Materials index cards

- Students should make sets of index cards with a unit of time on the front of the card—for example: *seconds*—and a unit (or mixed units) on the back side of the card—for example: *minutes*. They should include a quantity for one of the units—for example: *210* seconds. Students may choose units from the chart shown on page 623.

210 seconds

minutes

- A student selects a card from the stack and determines how to convert from the unit with a quantity to the unit on the back of the card.

## COMMON ERRORS

**Error** Students mix up A.M. and P.M. when finding elapsed time.

**Example** The elapsed time from 10:30 A.M. to 2:15 P.M. is 8 hr 15 min.

**Springboard to Learning** Have students find the total elapsed time as the *sum* of the elapsed times before and after 12:00 noon.

10:30 A.M. to 12:00 P.M. = 1 hr 30 min
12:00 P.M. to 2:15 P.M. = 2 hr 15 min
3 hr 45 min

## 3 EXPLAIN

### Share and Show 

The first problem connects to the learning model. Have students use the MathBoard to explain their thinking.

Use the checked exercises for **Quick Check**. Students should show their answers for the **Quick Check** on the MathBoards.

 Use **Math Talk** to focus on students' understanding of elapsed time.

- **How could you use an analog clock to find the length of the movie?** I would move forward on the clock from 1:35 to 3:40, which is 2 hours and 5 minutes.

 **Quick Check** 

 a student misses the checked exercises

 Differentiate Instruction with
- Reteach 10.7
- Personal Math Trainer 5.MD.A.1
- RtI Tier 1 Activity (online)

### On Your Own

To help students complete the conversions in Exercises 5–9, encourage them to use the table on page 623.

A variety of methods can be used to find the start, elapsed, or end times in Exercises 5–8. Have students share the methods they used.

---

Name ______________________

### Share and Show 

**Convert.**

1. 540 min = 9 hr
2. 8 d = 192 hr
3. 110 hr = 4 d 14 hr

**Find the end time.**

4. Start time: 9:17 A.M. Elapsed time: 5 hr 18 min End time: 2:35 P.M.

Math Talk — MATHEMATICAL PRACTICES 1 Make Sense of Problems How can you find how long a movie lasts if it starts at 1:35 P.M. and ends at 3:40 P.M.?

Possible answer: I would count the number of hours from 1:35 to 3:35 and then the number of minutes from 3:35 to 3:40. The movie lasts 2 hr 5 min.

### On Your Own

**Find the start, elapsed, or end time.**

5. Start time: 11:38 A.M.
Elapsed time: 3 hr 10 min
End time: 2:48 P.M.

6. Start time: 10:38 A.M.
Elapsed time: 2 hr 37 min
End time: 1:15 P.M.

7. Start time: 3:15 P.M.
Elapsed time: $2\frac{1}{4}$ hr
End time: 5:30 P.M.

8. Start time: 7:41 P.M.
Elapsed time: 1 hr 9 min
End time: 8:50 P.M.

9. WRITE Math **Explain** how you could find the number of seconds in a full 24-hour day. Then solve.
Possible explanation: I would multiply 24 hours by 60 minutes and then multiply my answer by 60 seconds. There are 86,400 seconds in a full day.

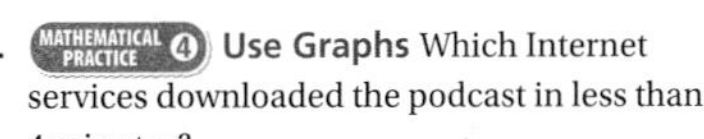

MATHEMATICAL PRACTICES MODEL • REASON • MAKE SENSE

## Problem Solving • Applications

For 10–12, use the graph.

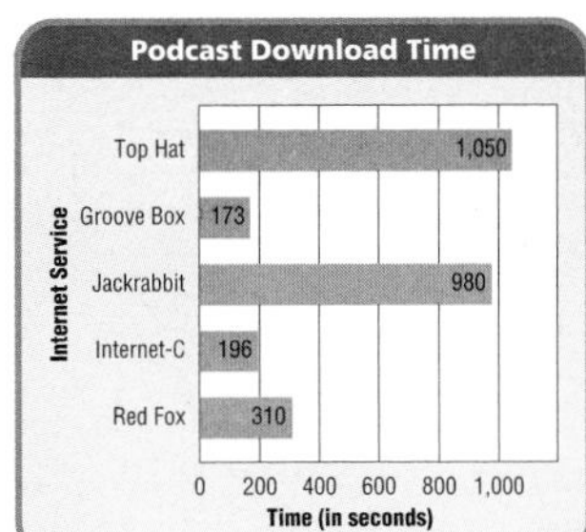


10.  Use Graphs Which Internet services downloaded the podcast in less than 4 minutes?

Groove Box and Internet-C

11. THINKSMARTER Which service took the longest to download the podcast? How much longer did it take than Red Fox in minutes and seconds?

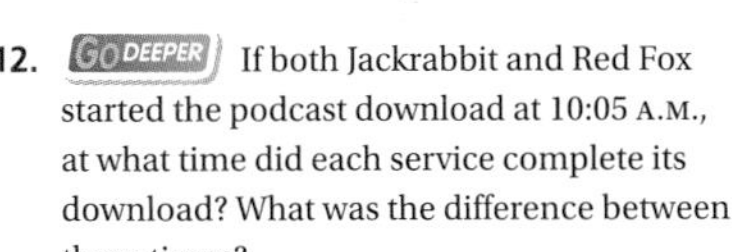

Top Hat; 12 min 20 sec

12. GO DEEPER If both Jackrabbit and Red Fox started the podcast download at 10:05 A.M., at what time did each service complete its download? What was the difference between these times?

Jackrabbit: 10:21 and 20 sec, Red Fox, 10:10 and 10 sec; 11 min 10 sec

Personal Math Trainer

13. THINKSMARTER+ Samit and his friends went to a movie at 7:30 P.M. The movie ended at 9:55 P.M. How long was the movie?

2 hours 25 minutes

Samit arrived home 35 minutes after the movie ended. What time did Samit get home? Explain how you found your answer.

10:30 P.M.; Possible explanation: I need to find 35 minutes after 9:55 P.M. It is 5 minutes until 10:00 P.M., so 30 minutes after 10:00 P.M. would be 10:30 P.M. So Samit arrived home at 10:30 P.M.





## DIFFERENTIATED INSTRUCTION | INDEPENDENT ACTIVITIES

Differentiated Centers Kit

*Activities*
***Measurement MATHO***

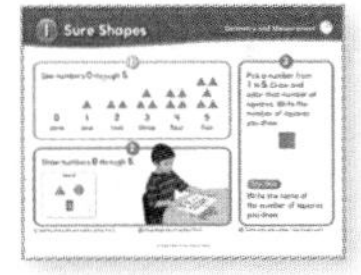

Students complete blue Activity Card 2 by choosing an appropriate metric unit for finding the length, mass, or capacity of an object.

*Literature*
***A Day in Dallas***

Students read the book and learn how to find elapsed time.

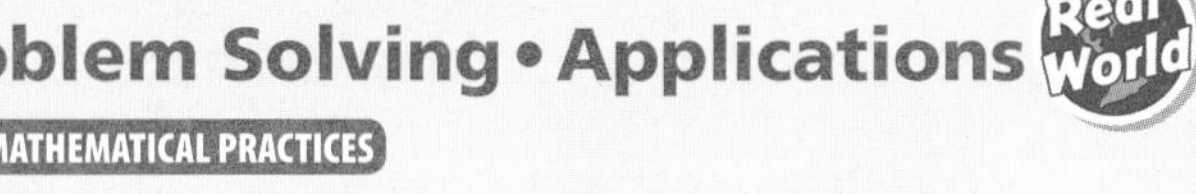

# 4 ELABORATE

## Problem Solving • Applications

MATHEMATICAL PRACTICES

THINKSMARTER

Problems 11 and 12 give students an opportunity to interpret and explain how increments on the bar graph are used to compare the services.

### Math on the Spot Video Tutor

Use this video to help students model and solve this type of *Think Smarter* problem.

**Math on the Spot** videos are in the Interactive Student Edition and at *www.thinkcentral.com*.

THINKSMARTER+ 

**Personal Math Trainer**

Be sure to assign this problem to students in the Personal Math Trainer. It features an animation to help them model and answer the problem. This item assesses a student's ability to solve multistep problems involving elapsed time. In the first part *A*, students must find the amount of time that has elapsed between two given times on a clock. If students answer with the incorrect elapsed time, they may not understand how to count on or subtract to find elapsed time. Students who have difficulty explaining their reasoning may need work with communicating math ideas.

# 5 EVALUATE Formative Assessment

## Essential Question

### Using the Language Objective

**Reflect** Have students discuss how you can solve elapsed time problems to answer the essential question.

**How can you solve elapsed time problems by converting units of time?** Possible answer: To convert, I use multiplication or division and a relationship like 1 hour = 60 minutes. Then I add or subtract units of time.

## Math Journal WRITE Math

**Write a real-world word problem that can be solved using elapsed time. Include the solution.**

## Practice and Homework

Use the Practice and Homework pages to provide students with more practice of the concepts and skills presented in this lesson. Students master their understanding as they complete practice items and then challenge their critical thinking skills with Problem Solving. Use the Write Math section to determine student's understanding of content for this lesson. Encourage students to use their Math Journals to record their answers.

Name ______________________

**Elapsed Time**

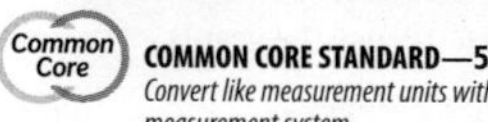


Common Core **COMMON CORE STANDARD—5.MD.A.1** *Convert like measurement units within a given measurement system.*

**Convert.**

1. 5 days = 120 hr
2. 8 hr = 480 min
3. 30 min = 1,800 s

**Think:** 1 day = 24 hours
$5 \times 24 = 120$

4. 15 hr = 900 min
5. 5 yr = 1,825 or 1,826 d
6. 7 d = 168 hr
7. 24 hr = 1,440 min
8. 600 s = 10 min
9. 60,000 min = 1,000 hr

**Find the start, elapsed, or end time.**

10. Start time: 11:00 A.M.
    Elapsed time: 4 hours 5 minutes
    End time: 3:05 P.M.

11. Start time: 6:30 P.M.
    Elapsed time: 2 hours 18 minutes
    End time: 8:48 P.M.

12. Start time: 8:15 A.M.
    Elapsed time: $9\frac{3}{4}$ hours
    End time: 6:00 P.M.

13. Start time: 2:00 P.M.
    Elapsed time: 6 hr 30 min, or $6\frac{1}{2}$ hr
    End time: 8:30 P.M.

### Problem Solving Real World

14. Kiera's dance class starts at 4:30 P.M. and ends at 6:15 P.M. How long is her dance class?
    1 hr 45 min

15. Julio watched a movie that started at 11:30 A.M. and ended at 2:12 P.M. How long was the movie?
    2 hr 42 min

16. WRITE Math Write a real-world word problem that can be solved using elapsed time. Include the solution.
    Check students' problems and solutions.





## Cross-Curricular

### SCIENCE

- A *gestation period* is the length of time it takes for an embryo to develop into a baby. Different animals have different gestation periods. The table below shows the average gestation periods of four mammals.
- Convert each gestation period in the table to weeks and days.

| Mammal | Gestation (days) |
| --- | --- |
| Asian elephant | 645 |
| Red fox | 52 |
| Llama | 330 |
| Porcupine | 112 |

Asian elephant, 92 wk 1 d; red fox, 7 wk 3 d; llama, 47 wk 1 d; porcupine, 16 wk

### SOCIAL STUDIES

- Many people volunteer in their neighborhoods and communities to improve government and society. This is one way that citizens can go beyond basic civil responsibilities to improve their community.
- Suppose that Samantha worked 420 minutes cleaning her local park. How many hours did Samantha spend cleaning?
  7 hours

## Lesson Check (5.MD.A.1)

1. Michelle went on a hike. She started on the trail at 6:45 A.M. and returned at 3:28 P.M. How long did she hike?

   8 hours 43 minutes

2. Grant started a marathon at 8:00 A.M. He took 4 hours 49 minutes to complete the marathon. When did he cross the finish line?

   12:49 P.M.

## Spiral Review (5.NBT.A.3b, 5.NF.A.1, 5.NF.B.6, 5.MD.A.1)

3. Molly is filling a pitcher that holds 2 gallons of water. She is filling the pitcher with a 1-cup measuring cup. How many times will she have to fill the 1-cup measuring cup to fill the pitcher?

   32 times

4. Choose a symbol to make the following statement true. Write >, <, or =.

   1.625 ◯ 1.7

   <

5. Adrian's recipe for raisin muffins calls for $1\frac{3}{4}$ cups raisins for one batch of muffins. Adrian wants to make $2\frac{1}{2}$ batches of the muffins for a bake sale. How many cups of raisins will Adrian use?

   $4\frac{3}{8}$ cups

6. Kevin is riding his bike on a $10\frac{1}{8}$-mile bike path. He has covered the first $5\frac{3}{4}$ miles already. How many miles does he have left to ride?

   $4\frac{3}{8}$ miles

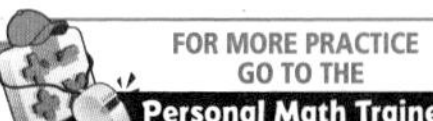

FOR MORE PRACTICE GO TO THE **Personal Math Trainer**





Continue concepts and skills practice with Lesson Check. Use Spiral Review to engage students in previously taught concepts and to promote content retention. Common Core standards are correlated to each section.

# Chapter 10 Review/Test

## Summative Assessment

Use the **Chapter Review/Test** to assess students' progress in Chapter 10.

You may want to review with students the essential question for the chapter.

### Chapter Essential Question

**What strategies can you use to compare and convert measurements?**

Ask the following questions to focus students' thinking:

- **How can you decide whether to multiply or divide when you are converting measurements?**
- **How can you organize your solution when you are solving a multistep measurement problem?**
- **How is converting metric measurements different from converting customary measurements?**

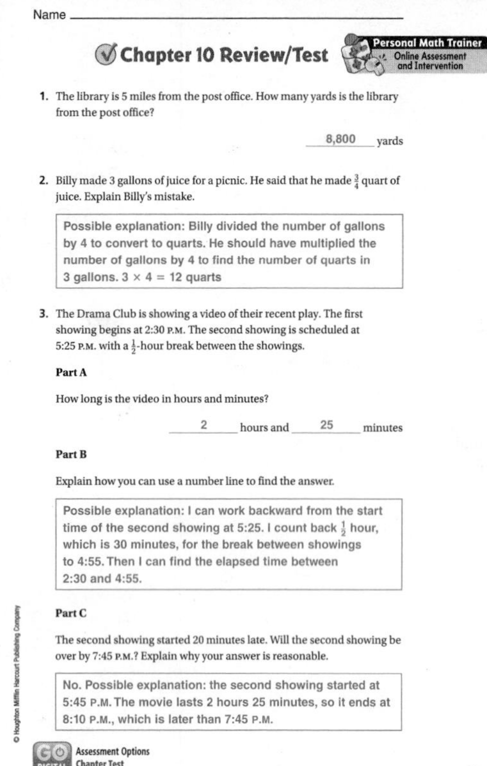
Name

Chapter 10 Review/Test — Personal Math Trainer: Online Assessment and Intervention

1. The library is 5 miles from the post office. How many yards is the library from the post office?

8,800 yards

2. Billy made 3 gallons of juice for a picnic. He said that he made $\frac{3}{4}$ quart of juice. Explain Billy's mistake.

Possible explanation: Billy divided the number of gallons by 4 to convert to quarts. He should have multiplied the number of gallons by 4 to find the number of quarts in 3 gallons. 3 × 4 = 12 quarts

3. The Drama Club is showing a video of their recent play. The first showing begins at 2:30 P.M. The second showing is scheduled at 5:25 P.M. with a $\frac{1}{2}$-hour break between the showings.

Part A

How long is the video in hours and minutes?

2 hours and 25 minutes

Part B

Explain how you can use a number line to find the answer.

Possible explanation: I can work backward from the start time of the second showing at 5:25. I count back $\frac{1}{2}$ hour, which is 30 minutes, for the break between showings to 4:55. Then I can find the elapsed time between 2:30 and 4:55.

Part C

The second showing started 20 minutes late. Will the second showing be over by 7:45 P.M.? Explain why your answer is reasonable.

No. Possible explanation: the second showing started at 5:45 P.M. The movie lasts 2 hours 25 minutes, so it ends at 8:10 P.M., which is later than 7:45 P.M.

GO DIGITAL Assessment Options Chapter Test

Chapter 10 629

4. Fred bought 4 liters of liquid laundry detergent, 3,250 milliliters of fabric softener, and 2.5 liters of bleach. For 4a–4e, select True or False for each statement.

| | | | |
|---|---|---|---|
| 4a. | Fred bought 75 milliliters more fabric softener than bleach. | ○ True | ● False |
| 4b. | Fred bought 1.75 liters more laundry detergent than bleach. | ○ True | ● False |
| 4c. | Fred bought 750 milliliters more fabric softener than bleach. | ● True | ○ False |
| 4d. | Fred bought 150 milliliters more laundry detergent than bleach. | ○ True | ● False |
| 4e. | Fred bought 0.75 liters more laundry detergent than fabric softener. | ● True | ○ False |

5. A male hippopotamus can weigh up to 10,000 pounds. How many tons is 10,000 pounds?

5 tons

6. THINKSMARTER+ Amar and his friends went to a movie at 4:45 P.M. The movie ended at 6:20 P.M.

Part A

How long was the movie?

1 hours and 35 minutes

Part B

Amar got home 45 minutes after the movie ended. What time did Amar get home? Explain how you found your answer.

7:05 P.M.; Possible explanation: I need to find 45 minutes after 6:20 P.M. 6:20 to 7:00 is 40 minutes, so 5 minutes more is 7:05.

630

## Data-Driven Decision Making RtI

## Chapter 10

Based on the results of the Chapter Review/Test use the following resources to review skills.

| Item | Lesson | Standard | Content Focus | Personal Math Trainer | Intervene With |
|---|---|---|---|---|---|
| 1, 11, 16, 18 | 10.1, 10.4 | 5.MD.A.1 | Convert among different-sized customary units of length. | 5.MD.A.1 | R—10.1, R—10.4 |
| 2, 7, 10, 15, 17 | 10.2, 10.4 | 5.MD.A.1 | Convert among different-sized customary units of capacity. | 5.MD.A. 1 | R—10.2, R—10.4 |
| 3, 6 | 10.7 | 5.MD.A.1 | Calculate elapsed time by converting between hours and minutes when necessary. | 5.MD.A. 1 | R—10.7 |
| 4, 8, 13 | 10.5 | 5.MD.A.1 | Convert among different-sized metric units of length, capacity, or mass. | 5.MD.A. 1 | R—10.5 |
| 5, 12, 20, 22 | 10.3 | 5.MD.A.1 | Convert among different-sized units of weight. | 5.MD.A. 1 | R—10.3 |
| 14, 21 | 10.6 | 5.MD.A.1 | Solve multi-step measurement problems involving conversion of units within the metric measurement system. | 5.MD.A. 1 | R—10.6 |
| 19 | 10.7 | 5.MD.A.1 | Convert among different-sized units of time. | 5.MD.A. 1 | R—10.7 |

**Key:** R—Reteach (in the *Chapter Resources*)

Name ___

7. Select the objects that hold the same amount of liquid as a 96-fluid-ounce jug. Mark all that apply.

- (A) three 1-quart bottles
- (B) two 1-quart bottles
- (C) two 1-quart bottles and two 1-pint bottles
- (D) one 1-quart bottle and eight 8-ounce fluid glasses
- (E) two 8-ounce fluid glasses and two 1-pint bottles

8. Lorena's backpack has a mass of 3,000 grams. What is the mass of Lorena's backpack in kilograms?

3 kilograms

9. GO DEEPER Richard walks every day for exercise at a rate of 1 kilometer every 12 minutes.

**Part A**

At this rate, how many meters can Richard walk in 1 hour? Explain how you found your answer.

5,000 meters; Possible explanation: Since there are 60 minutes in 1 hour, I divided 60 ÷ 12 = 5. Then I multiplied 1 × 5 = 5 to find out how many kilometers Richard walks in 1 hour. Since there are 1,000 meters in 1 kilometer, I multiplied 5 × 1,000 = 5,000 to convert to meters.

**Part B**

Suppose Richard walks 1 kilometer every 10 minutes. How many meters further can he walk in 1 hour at this new rate? Explain how you found your answer.

1,000 meters; Possible explanation: Since there are 60 minutes in 1 hour, I divided 60 ÷ 10 = 6. Then I multiplied 1 × 6 = 6 to find out how many kilometers Richard walks in 1 hour. Since there are 1,000 meters in 1 kilometer, I multiplied 6 × 1,000 = 6,000 to convert to meters. So, Richard walks 6,000 meters in 1 hour at his new rate. Then I subtracted 6,000 − 5,000 = 1,000.





10. Beth filled 32 jars with paint. If each jar holds 1 pint of paint, how many gallons of paint did Beth use?

4 gallons

11. Griffins's driveway is 36 feet long. Choose the word and number to complete the sentence correctly.

To convert 36 feet to yards, [add / subtract / multiply / **divide**] 36 by [**3** / 12 / 1,760 / 5,280].

12. Carlos bought 5 pounds of carrots. How many ounces of carrots did he buy?

80 ounces

13. Chandler has 824 millimeters of fabric. How many centimeters of fabric does Chandler have? Use the numbers and symbols on the tiles to write an equation to show the conversion.

824 | 8.24 | 82.4 | 0.824

× | ÷ | =

10 | 100 | 1,000

824 ÷ 10 = 82.4

Chandler has 82.4 centimeters of fabric.

14. Glenn needs to cut pieces of ribbon that are each 1 meter long to make ribbon key chains. If he has 3 pieces of ribbon that are each 1 dekameter long, how many 1-meter pieces of ribbon can he cut?

30 pieces





## Performance Assessment Task

### Chapter 10

See the *Chapter Resources* for a Performance Task that assesses students' understanding of the content of this chapter.

For each task, you will find sample student work for each of the response levels in the task scoring rubric.

Portfolio Performance Assessment Tasks may be used for portfolios.

Be sure to assign students Exercise 6 in the Personal Math Trainer. It features an animation or video to help students model and solve the problem.



Name ___

15. A large pot holds 8 quarts of spaghetti sauce. Lisa has 1-pint containers of spaghetti sauce. Complete the table to help you find the number of 1-pint containers of spaghetti sauce Lisa will need to fill the pot.

| quart | 2 | 4 | 6 | 8 |
|---|---|---|---|---|
| pint | 4 | 8 | 12 | 16 |

Lisa will need 16 1-pint containers to fill the pot.

16. Emily bought 48 yards of fabric to make curtains. How many inches of fabric did Emily buy?

1,728 inches

17. Kelly is having a party. She wants to make punch. The recipe for punch uses 3 pints of pineapple juice, 5 cups of orange juice, $\frac{1}{4}$ gallon of lemonade, and 1 quart of apricot nectar.

**Part A**

Kelly says her recipe will make 20 cups of punch. Is Kelly correct? Explain your answer.

No. The recipe will make 19 cups of punch. Possible explanation: I converted all the measurements to cups: 3 pints of pineapple juice = 6 cups; $\frac{1}{4}$ gallon of lemonade = 4 cups, 1 quart of apricot nectar = 4 cups. Then I found the total number of cups including the 5 cups of orange juice: 6 + 5 + 4 + 4 = 19 cups.

**Part B**

Kelly decides to pour her punch into 1-quart containers to fit into her refrigerator until the party starts. She has four 1-quart containers. Will all of her punch fit into the containers? Explain.

No. Possible explanation: one 1-quart container will hold 4 cups of punch. Four 1-quart containers will hold 16 cups of punch. Kelly has 19 cups of punch. Since 19 > 16, all of the punch will not fit into the four 1-quart containers.





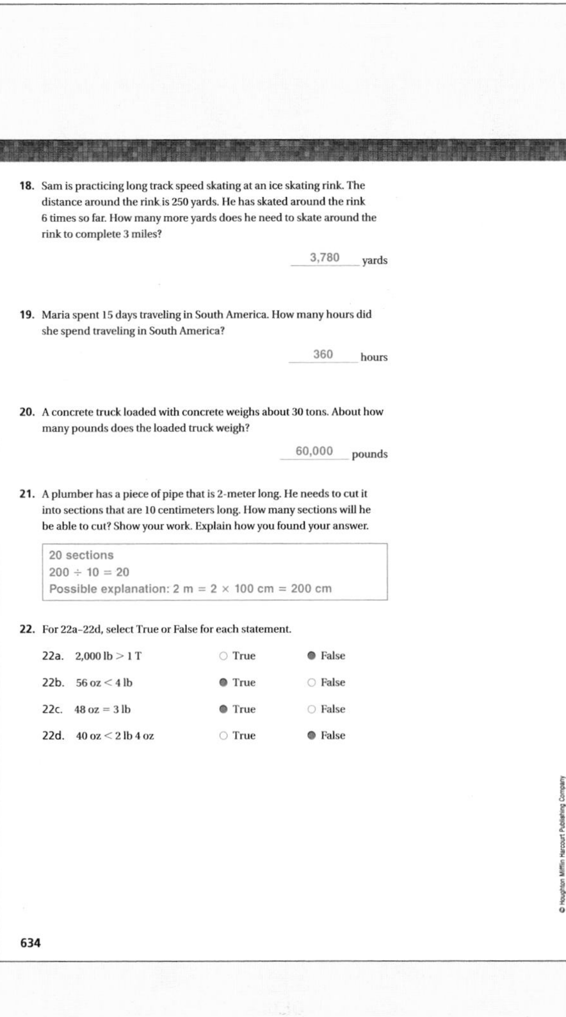

18. Sam is practicing long track speed skating at an ice skating rink. The distance around the rink is 250 yards. He has skated around the rink 6 times so far. How many more yards does he need to skate around the rink to complete 3 miles?

3,780 yards

19. Maria spent 15 days traveling in South America. How many hours did she spend traveling in South America?

360 hours

20. A concrete truck loaded with concrete weighs about 30 tons. About how many pounds does the loaded truck weigh?

60,000 pounds

21. A plumber has a piece of pipe that is 2-meter long. He needs to cut it into sections that are 10 centimeters long. How many sections will he be able to cut? Show your work. Explain how you found your answer.

20 sections
200 ÷ 10 = 20
Possible explanation: 2 m = 2 × 100 cm = 200 cm

22. For 22a–22d, select True or False for each statement.

| | | True | False |
|---|---|---|---|
| 22a. | 2,000 lb > 1 T | ○ True | ● False |
| 22b. | 56 oz < 4 lb | ● True | ○ False |
| 22c. | 48 oz = 3 lb | ● True | ○ False |
| 22d. | 40 oz < 2 lb 4 oz | ○ True | ● False |

# Chapter 10 Test

## Summative Assessment

Use the **Chapter Test** to assess students' progress in Chapter 10.

Chapter Tests are presented in Common Core assessment formats in the *Chapter Resources*

**Personal Math Trainer**

Name ________________ | Chapter 10 Test Page 1

1. The first bus stop on a bus route is 4 miles from school. How many yards is the first bus stop from school?

   7,040 yards

2. John made 2 quarts of juice for a school party. He said that he made $\frac{2}{4}$ cup of juice. Explain John's mistake.

   Possible explanation: John divided the number of quarts by 4 to convert to cups. He should have multiplied the number of quarts by 4 to find the number of cups in 2 quarts. $2 \times 4 = 8$ cups

3. The debate team is showing a video of their recent debate. The first showing begins at 3:15 P.M. The second showing is scheduled at 4:50 P.M. with a $\frac{1}{2}$-hour break between the showings.

   **Part A**

   How long is the video in hours and minutes?

   1 hour(s) and 5 minutes

   **Part B**

   Explain how you can use a number line to find the answer.

   Possible explanation: I can work backward from the start time of the second showing at 4:50. I count back $\frac{1}{2}$ hour, which is 30 minutes, for the break between showings to 4:20. Then I can find the elapsed time between 3:15 and 4:20.

   **Part C**

   The second showing started 20 minutes late. Will the second showing be over by 6:30 P.M.? Explain why your answer is reasonable.

   Yes. Possible explanation: the second showing started at 5:10 P.M. The video lasts 1 hour 5 minutes, so it ends at 6:15 P.M., which is earlier than 6:30 P.M.

GO ON

Chapter Resources 10-19 Chapter 10 Test
© Houghton Mifflin Harcourt Publishing Company

Name ________________ | Chapter 10 Test Page 2

4. Ed bought 3 liters of water, 2,750 milliliters of sports drink, and 2.25 liters of juice. For numbers 4a–4e, select True or False for each statement.

   4a. Ed bought 250 milliliters more water than sports drink. ● True ○ False

   4b. Ed bought 1.25 liters more water than juice. ○ True ● False

   4c. Ed bought 50 milliliters more sports drink than juice. ○ True ● False

   4d. Ed bought 0.5 liter more of sports drink than juice. ● True ○ False

   4e. Ed bought 75 milliliters more water than juice. ○ True ● False

5. A female elephant can weigh up to 8,000 pounds. How many tons is 8,000 pounds?

   4 tons

6. Ushma and her friends went to a movie that started at 7:35 P.M. The movie ended at 9:20 P.M.

   **Part A**

   How long was the movie?

   1 hour(s) and 45 minutes

   **Part B**

   Ushma got home 50 minutes after the movie ended. What time did Ushma get home? Explain how you found your answer.

   10:10 P.M.; Possible explanation: I need to find 50 minutes after 9:20 P.M. 9:20 to 10:00 is 40 minutes, so 10 minutes more is 10:10.

GO ON

Chapter Resources 10-20 Chapter 10 Test
© Houghton Mifflin Harcourt Publishing Company

## Data-Driven Decision Making RtI

Based on the results of the Chapter Test use the following resources to review skills.

| Item | Lesson | Standard | Content Focus | Personal Math Trainer | Intervene With |
|---|---|---|---|---|---|
| 1, 11, 16 | 10.1 | 5.MD.A.1 | Convert among different-sized customary units of length. | 5.MD.A.1 | R—10.1 |
| 2, 7 | 10.2 | 5.MD.A.1 | Convert among different-sized customary units of capacity. | 5.MD.A.1 | R—10.2 |
| 3, 6 | 10.7 | 5.MD.A.1 | Calculate elapsed time by converting between hours and minutes when necessary. | 5.MD.A.1 | R—10.7 |
| 4, 8, 13 | 10.5 | 5.MD.A.1 | Convert among different-sized metric units of length, capacity, or mass. | 5.MD.A.1 | R—10.5 |
| 5, 12, 20, 22 | 10.3 | 5.MD.A.1 | Convert among different-sized units of weight. | 5.MD.A.1 | R—10.3 |
| 9, 14, 21 | 10.6 | 5.MD.A.1 | Solve multi-step measurement problems involving conversion of units within the metric measurement system. | 5.MD.A.1 | R—10.6 |
| 10, 15, 17, 18 | 10.4 | 5.MD.A.1 | Solve multi-step measurement problems involving conversion of units within the customary measurement system. | 5.MD.A.1 | R—10.4 |
| 19 | 10.7 | 5.MD.A.1 | Convert among different-sized units of time. | 5.MD.A.1 | R—10.7 |

**Key:** R—Reteach (in the *Chapter Resources*)

Name ______________

Chapter 10 Test
Page 3

**7.** Select the objects that hold the same amount of liquid as a 128-fluid-ounce jug. Mark all that apply.

(A) two 1-quart bottles

(B) four 1-quart bottles

(C) two 8-ounce fluid glasses and two 1-quart bottles

(D) one 1-quart bottle and twelve 8-ounce fluid glasses

(E) two 1-quart bottles and four 1-pint bottles

**8.** Roland's suitcase has a mass of 2,500 dekagrams. What is the mass of Roland's suitcase in kilograms?

25 kilograms

**9.** Monica walks every day for exercise at a rate of 1 kilometer every 20 minutes.

**Part A**

At this rate, how many meters can Monica walk in 1 hour? Explain how you found your answer.

3,000 meters; Possible explanation: Since there are 60 minutes in 1 hour, I would divide $60 \div 20 = 3$. Then I would multiply $1 \times 3 = 3$ to find out how many kilometers Monica walks in 1 hour. Since there are 1,000 meters in 1 kilometer, I would multiply $3 \times 1{,}000 = 3{,}000$ to convert to meters.

**Part B**

Suppose Monica walks 1 kilometer every 15 minutes. How many meters further can she walk in 1 hour at this new rate? Explain how you found your answer.

1,000 meters; Possible explanation: Since there are 60 minutes in 1 hour, I would divide $60 \div 15 = 4$. Then I would multiply $1 \times 4 = 4$ to find out how many kilometers Monica walks in 1 hour. Since there are 1,000 meters in 1 kilometer, I would multiply $4 \times 1{,}000 = 4{,}000$ to convert to meters. So, Monica walks 4,000 meters in 1 hour at her new rate. Then I subtract $4{,}000 - 3{,}000 = 1{,}000$.

GO ON




Name ______________

Chapter 10 Test
Page 4

**10.** Mrs. Davis has 64 bottles of water. If each bottle holds 1 pint of water, how many gallons of water does Mrs. Davis have?

8 gallons

**11.** The distance between second base and third base on a regulation baseball field is 30 yards. Choose the word and number to complete the sentence correctly.

To convert 30 yards to feet, [add / subtract / **multiply** / divide] 30 by [**3** / 12 / 1,760 / 5,280].

**12.** Keiko bought 3 pounds of fruit salad. How many ounces of fruit salad did Keiko buy?

48 ounces

**13.** Anoki bought 360 millimeters of fabric. How many centimeters of fabric does Anoki have? Use the numbers and symbols on the tiles to write an equation to show the conversion.

360 | 36.0 | 3.60 | 0.360

× | ÷ | =

10 | 100 | 1,000

$360 \div 10 = 36.0$

Anoki has 36.0 centimeters of fabric.

**14.** Mickey needs to cut pieces of ribbon that are each 1-meter long to tie onto balloons. If he has 8 pieces of ribbon that are each 1 dekameter long, how many 1-meter pieces of ribbon can he cut?

80 pieces

GO ON




Name ______________

Chapter 10 Test
Page 5

**15.** A fish tank holds 15 gallons of water. Jordan is using a 1-pint container to fill the fish tank. Complete the table to help you find the number of pints of water Jordan will need to fill the fish tank.

| gallon | 1 | 5 | 10 | 15 |
|---|---|---|---|---|
| pint | 8 | 40 | 80 | 120 |

Jordan will need 120 pints to fill the fish tank.

**16.** Bradley bought 36 yards of fabric to make costumes for the school play. How many inches of fabric did Bradley buy?

1,296 inches

**17.** Joann is having a party. She wants to make punch. The recipe for punch uses 4 pints of orange juice, 5 cups of apple juice, $\frac{1}{2}$ gallon of lemonade, and 2 quarts of pineapple juice.

**Part A**

Joann says her recipe will make 30 cups of punch. Is Joann correct? Explain your answer.

No. The recipe will make 29 cups of punch. Possible explanation: I converted all the measurements to cups: 4 pints of orange juice = 8 cups; $\frac{1}{2}$ gallon of lemonade = 8 cups, 2 quarts of pineapple juice = 8 cups. Then I found the total number of cups including the 5 cups of apple juice: $8 + 5 + 8 + 8 = 29$ cups.

**Part B**

Joann decides to pour her punch into 1-quart containers to fit into her refrigerator until the party starts. She has eight 1-quart containers. Will all of her punch fit into the containers? Explain.

Yes. Possible explanation: one 1-quart container will hold 4 cups of punch. Eight 1-quart containers will hold 32 cups of punch. Joann has 29 cups of punch. Since $32 > 29$, all of the punch will fit into the eight 1-quart containers.

GO ON




Name ______________

Chapter 10 Test
Page 6

**18.** Keisha is walking around a track that is 400 yards long. She has walked around the track 5 times so far. How many more yards does she need to walk around the track to complete 2 miles?

1,520 yards

**19.** Betsy spent 26 days traveling in Europe. How many hours did she spend traveling in Europe?

624 hours

**20.** The average weight of a gray whale is 16 tons. About how many pounds does a gray whale weigh?

32,000 pounds

**21.** An art teacher has a roll of mural paper that is 5 meters long. She needs to cut it into 1-decimeter long pieces for a collage project. How many 1-decimeter pieces can she cut from the roll of mural paper? Show your work. Explain how you found your answer.

50 pieces
Possible explanation: $5 \text{ m} \times 10 = 50$ decimeters

**22.** For numbers 22a–22d, select True or False for each statement.

| | Statement | True | False |
|---|---|---|---|
| 16a. | 1,000 lb > 1 T | ○ | ● |
| 16b. | 40 oz < 3 lb | ● | ○ |
| 16c. | 36 oz = 2 lb | ○ | ● |
| 16d. | 68 oz < 4 lb 6 oz | ● | ○ |

STOP




Portfolio

## Portfolio Suggestions

The portfolio represents the growth, talents, achievements, and reflections of the mathematics learner. Students might spend a short time selecting work samples for their portfolios.

You may want to have students respond to the following questions:

- What new understanding of math have I developed in the past several weeks?
- What growth in understanding or skills can I see in my work?
- What can I do to improve my understanding of math ideas?
- What would I like to learn more about?

For information about how to organize, share, and evaluate portfolios, see the *Chapter Resources*.